LIFESENSE

LIFESENSE

OUR LIVES THROUGH
ANIMAL EYES

JOHN DOWNER

BBC BOOKS

ACKNOWLEDGEMENTS

This book is a companion to the BBC television series *Lifesense*. Such a project is inevitably a collaboration, and I am especially grateful for the immense contribution made by every member of the production team. Assistant producers Steve Nichols and Rupert Barrington have given countless ideas and unearthed many of the stories. Researcher Tania Dorrity has been involved from the inception of the project and helped develop and verify the themes. Researcher Neil Lucas has contributed in a practical way in bringing the stories to life

At BBC Books, Sheila Ableman, Nicky Copeland and Jennifer Fry have worked on the book with skill and judgement. In particular, Kay Hyman deserves special thanks for her commitment and advice.

The *Lifesense* project has drawn on the research of scientists and scholars from many different disciplines throughout the world. Invariably our enquiries have been met with invaluable suggestions and guidance. I am indebted to everyone who gave their help so generously.

PICTURE CREDITS

Ardea (François Gohier) page 67; **Jack Barrie** pages 74–5; **Rupert Barrington** pages 149 and 207; **Ron Boardman** page 178; **Bruce Coleman** pages 38 (Michael Price) and 201 (Norman Tomalin); **Sue Cunningham** pages 214 and 217; **Martin Dohrn** front cover and pages 40 and 104; **Mark Edwards/Still Pictures** pages 212–13; **Michael and Patricia Fogden** page 64; **Sarah Ford** jacket flap; **Sonia Halliday Photographs** (Barry Searle) page 147; **Robert Harding** (Robin Hanbury Tenison) page 107; **Dick Klees** page 35; **Frank Lane** (Maslowski) page 10; **Richard Mills** page 39; **NHPA** (Stephen Dalton) pages 15, 25 and 49; **Oxford Scientific Films** pages 21 (Frank Schneidermeyer), 51 (top, G. I. Bernard), 52–3 (Richard Packwood), 115 (Martyn Chillmaid) and 209 (David Wright); **Robert Peck** page 151; **Science Photo Library** pages 16, 161, 169 (all David Scharf) and 174 (CNRI); **Frank Spooner/Gamma** (Sallaz) page 203; **Survival Anglia** (Jen and Des Bartlett) page 71; **ZEFA** pages 26, 31 and 210 (Heilman). All remaining photographs were taken by John Downer.

Front cover photograph by Martin Dohrn shows a peregrine falcon in New York
Back cover photograph by John Downer shows a sacred cow in Varanasi

Published by BBC Books,
a division of BBC Enterprises Limited,
Woodlands, 80 Wood Lane, London W12 0TT
First published 1991
© John Downer 1991
ISBN 0 563 36115 8
Designed by Bill Mason
Set in Baskerville by Butler & Tanner Ltd, Frome
Printed and bound in Great Britain by Butler & Tanner Ltd, Frome
Colour separations by Technik Ltd, Berkhamstead
Jacket printed by Lawrence Allen Ltd, Weston-super-Mare

CONTENTS

Introduction

THE BBC TV SERIES *LIFESENSE* developed out of *Supersense*. The previous series had explored the remarkable world of animal senses, presented from the unusual viewpoint of the creatures themselves. This idea naturally progressed into *Lifesense*, inspired by the belief that the relationship between animals and ourselves could also be viewed afresh from this unique perspective.

What exactly is the animal's view? Fortunately, science can now tell us how most animals interpret the world, as research has revealed much about their senses. I have used this information, where possible, to provide an impression of how we are actually perceived by other creatures.

But the viewpoint is more than this. It encompasses how animals behave and the influence of our actions on their behaviour. More significantly, it is also about how whole populations of animals and plants are affected by human lives and attitudes.

The book does not attempt to be fully comprehensive – animals are so central to people's lives that the number and nuances of relationships are almost infinite. However, I hope it presents a framework that will allow other examples to be placed into context.

As research for the series and the book developed, it became clear that the issue concerned not simply our relationship with other organisms, but something far more profound. Humans have been on earth for around a million years and throughout this time our lives have been entwined with those of other creatures. It was increasingly obvious as the story unravelled that animals and plants have not only affected all the stages of human existence but have also been the catalysts for them.

The major steps were taken via the partnerships forged with plants and animals that we now recognise as agriculture and domestication. These practices allowed people to live away from the natural world, increase their populations and develop civilisations. Therefore, the description of our changing relationships with other organisms is also an account of human

history. The novel perspective provided by the animals and plants involved allows the events to be interpreted as if through new eyes.

Sometimes, in recounting this narrative, developments that in fact took a very long time inevitably appear compressed. This could create the impression that animals and plants made conscious decisions as they modified their relationships with us. But in all cases the partnerships arose through the constant evolutionary pressure that motivates all change in the natural world. What might be surprising is that the we too were subjected to the same evolutionary forces. Because of a belief in our superior intellect, we arrogantly assume that we must have deliberately set about abandoning our original hunter-gathering way of life. But this was far from the case. The transitions took place automatically as existing relationships with the life around us became more complex.

To grasp the beginnings of the story it is not necessary to delve back into prehistory. Living representatives of the past can be found today among disappearing tribal cultures that still maintain our ancestors' way of life. It proved an opportune time to make *Lifesense*, as it soon became clear that this primeval lifestyle would not survive for much longer. To find the few examples that still remain, the series explored the cultures of over 20 countries, many in remote regions of the world. Most of the descriptions contained in this book are first-hand accounts of these experiences, although often rendered from the perspective of the associated animals.

It soon became apparent that cultures still living close to nature intuitively appreciate the significance of other life and treat it with respect. The same reverential view is maintained by people whose lives revolve round their livestock. It was only when human populations, supplied by domesticated animals and cultivated plants, were able to live isolated from the world that sustained them, that this understanding and respect broke down.

But even our modern lives are inextricably linked to other organisms. They still not only supply us with food but they also enter our homes, live on our bodies and even influence climate and the air we breathe. An appreciation of the significance of these relationships has relevance to the ecology of the whole planet. What we can learn from the past can help us understand the precarious nature of our present lives. We could never exist without other organisms and they are never far from us. As the first chapter shows, some of the animals that scavenged from our distant ancestors and entered their cave-dwellings can still be found in our homes today.

A young rhesus macaque in a Hindu temple peers out on the human world.

CHAPTER
I

HOME LIFE

ACH MORNING, AS THE rising sun starts to warm the East African savannah, roosting vultures begin to stir. Marooned on the acacia trees, they wait until the sun forms invisible elevators from floating pockets of warmed air. The birds flap laboriously towards these thermals and, once in the uplift, their heavy bodies are transported effortlessly to heights of 3 000 metres or more.

From this vantage point their keen eyes, with telephoto vision, look for a freshly killed meal. They survey the Great Rift valley below, a landscape that a million years ago cradled the emerging human race. The vultures follow the activities of hunters and other scavengers, who are enacting a ritual little changed since that early time. Today, as in the past, scavengers find food by observing the flight paths of the vultures – these watching eyes are often human.

A spiral of soaring vultures signals the position of a lion kill. Most scavengers wait for the lions to depart but the tribesmen move in quickly. The lions, engrossed at tearing at their carcass and fearing few predators, rarely notice as the humans creep towards them. Lightly armed, the men are no match for a pride of lions so they are not planning a surprise attack. Instead they are playing a game of bluff.

Once they have come within range, the tribesmen's stealth changes to bravado. Waving spears and rattling sticks, they run towards the lions, which, confronted by this psychological warfare, invariably take the safer course and retreat.

Opposite: In North America garbage cans provide free takeaways for marauding parties of urban raccoons.
Overleaf: In Africa lions are sometimes driven from the kill by tribesmen seeking fresh meat. Such scavenging would have supplemented the diet of early humans.

The human scavengers have only a limited time to claim their prize, for such deceit can be no more than temporary. Once a haunch of meat has been taken, the lions are quick to return. The vultures are often even faster, dropping like darts as the people depart. Attracted by all this activity, hyenas and jackals also join in the scrum and, on the sidelines, black kites dive down to pick up scraps.

This primal scene, still witnessed in parts of Africa, was common when the human race survived by hunting and scavenging. Our fellow scavengers from those times are still with us today, joined by creatures that have taken to living in our houses. Animals have accompanied humans in their journey towards civilisation – via caves, wooden shelters, stone buildings, cities. In the process our existence has been transformed, and with it, inevitably, the lives of other species.

FLY'S-EYE VIEW

HOUSEFLIES ARE DRAWN TO modern human homes, just as they once visited those of our ancestors, responding to the chemical odours that signify even the slightest degree of decay. In addition, unlike most flies, which are attracted to light, the housefly seeks shade. This preference once guided the fly into human cave-dwellings and steers it into our houses today. The fly observes our world through bulbous compound eyes, which break down the scene into a coarse, granulated view of varying shades. To the fly the dark shape of an open window is as welcoming as a cave entrance.

Once inside, the similarity ends, for the fly now has to cope with an environment artificially illuminated for human eyes. The fluorescent tubes that often light our homes actually flash on and off 50 times a second in sympathy with the alternating electric current. We never notice these fluctuations as our eyes cannot discern such small time intervals. However, the fly's eyes react far more quickly and to them the room appears lit by a pulsating strobe. As it buzzes around the human occupants, the fly has to cope with this distracting cycle of light and darkness.

Fortunately for the fly, its superior time perception also makes it difficult to swat. It finds our fastest actions laboriously slow and can easily avoid our clumsy attempts to remove it from our lives.

Though we never welcome the fly's company, through its association with us it has become one of the most widespread and successful of all animals. Many other creatures have similarly adapted their lives to ours and some have even taken up permanent residence with us. A great number of these lodgers are nest-dwellers.

Of all the great apes, humans are the only ones to build permanent nests.

*The housefly finds twentieth-century homes just as enticing as
the cave-dwellings of our ancestors.*

Like the homes of mice and birds, our houses shelter a hidden population of
other nest-dwelling organisms that survive by consuming either the nest-
lining directly or remnants of skin or hair shed by the host. From the point
of view of these nest-dwellers, little has changed since prehistoric times. The
blankets and sheets that we wrap round ourselves at night are even now
made from animal or plant products and we continue to line our nests with
fur or wool, even though they are now woven into decorative rugs and
carpets.

THE CARPETBAGGERS

SEVERAL INSECTS HAVE READILY adopted a lifestyle of deep-pile luxury in the heart of our homes. The tiny beige and black carpet beetles acquired their name through their habit of laying eggs on furnishings. Their larvae, covered with golden-brown hairs, are known as 'woolly bears'. They usually dwell in rugs and carpets but are equally at home among stored woollen and fur garments.

These larvae prefer soiled fibres and suffer from malnutrition in the carpets of the obsessively house-proud. However, when the going gets tough, they can survive as long as 10 months without eating. Even in the luxury of a dirty carpet, the woolly bears may take nine months to reach maturity. They then turn into pupae, among the carpet fibres, and emerge as adults two to three weeks later. The beetles find their way outside by flying towards the light, then seek out flowers and feed from pollen and nectar.

The carpet beetle is not found in every home but there are other nest-dwellers that are. When we go to bed every one of us snuggles down with an army of unseen companions.

STRANGE BEDFELLOWS

BENEATH THE SHEETS OF EVEN the cleanest bed lurk thousands of eight-legged scavengers. Each of us is responsible for sustaining a teeming population that depends on our nightly company for survival. We never notice our uninvited guests because each one is smaller than a speck of dust.

These dustmites are microscopic relatives of spiders and to them the mattress represents the limits of their known world. Many experience their whole lives under a single mattress stud. They are only able to survive in this seemingly barren landscape because each night cells flake from our skin surface and shower down on them like manna from heaven.

Every hour 400 million of these skin cells are discarded by each human being, wafting up on the warm air of our bodies and finally settling as the dust that covers the furniture of every home. As we undress we create a further blizzard of cells, the greatest quantity ensuing from the electrostatic storm whipped up when tights or socks are removed. As we sleep the skin flakes continue to fall, drifting through the weave of the bedclothes to the dustmites waiting below.

A revealing view of one of our unseen bed companions.
Up to two million dustmites inhabit the average
double bed.

Sustained by this nutritious snowstorm, up to two million dustmites are able to survive in the average mattress. As they graze the vast savannah of our sheets, like herds of miniature wildebeest, the dustmites attract hunters. Here the diminutive equivalent of lions are a type of predatory mite. These stalk the bed linen, using formidable jaws to pounce on the unsuspecting dustmites and suck them dry.

Except for such life and death struggles, the mites usually lead peaceful lives, disturbed only by bouts of human activity. Some of this exertion actually benefits the mites for it has recently been discovered that they reach their greatest numbers in the beds of sexually active adults. Even dustmites find a monotonous diet of skin cells lacking in nourishment and they derive a welcome source of additional protein from traces of spilt semen.

Compared with their human bedfellows the sex life of the dustmites is far from intimate: the male simply leaves his sperm in a package which the female picks up later.

After voracious feeding on our skin and secretions, the dustmites excrete in quantity. Around 20 pellets of processed skin cells pass through each mite every day. This fine dust adds to the pile of mummified carcasses of dead mites and their cast-off skins that soon accumulate in well-used beds. This debris, tossed into the air by a bed-maker, often induces a fit of sneezing.

The allergic reaction is so severe in some people it can trigger an asthma attack – in fact, the majority of such attacks are believed to be caused by dustmites. Their significance became apparent when European clothes and blankets were taken to Papua New Guinea, where the original tribes have survived until recently with few garments except those made from leaves and grasses. There was an outbreak of asthma as the local inhabitants became exposed to the new organism.

Early humans similarly wore little clothing apart from the occasional fur. But as people spread into colder parts of the world they began to protect themselves with woven fabrics. This portable nesting material attracted other species of nest-dwellers.

TASTE IN CLOTHES

CLOTHES MOTHS WERE ORIGINALLY confined to the nests of birds, but stored garments provide the same resources of food and shelter and several species of moth have adapted to a life in wardrobes and drawers. The adults are small brown moths that tend to scurry away from the light when a cupboard door is opened. Only the larvae actually consume the fibres of the clothes but they are rarely seen as they have an ingenious camouflage.

The caterpillar of the case-bearing clothes moth performs its vanishing

In an attempt at camouflage, case-bearing clothes moths weave their own striking costumes from the wool of jumpers.

trick by using wool fibres to spin its own matching sweater. It produces silken thread with which it weaves fragments of wool around its body. Caterpillars that live on green woollens knit green jumpers, those on red woollens knit red jumpers, while those on multicoloured woollens create a corresponding designer collection of different outfits. Although each caterpillar is beautifully matched to its immediate area, the colour coordination breaks down when they begin to move about. The disguise originated when the case-bearing moth lived solely in the nests of birds. Then the camouflage suit was created from nesting material and concealed the caterpillar from its host.

The case-bearer still thrives in the nests of birds but the most familiar clothes moth of northern Europe has taken to a life exclusively in human nests. The common clothes moth lacks the sartorial perfection of the case-bearer but its creamy-white caterpillar is equally hard to find. It conceals itself in a tube tunnelled through the weave of woollen cloth. Protected inside its cosy cocoon the larva grows to nearly a centimetre in length before it finally pupates into the adult moth. This development can take less than a month, but in cool conditions or when the quality of food is poor the process may last over a year.

The caterpillar's taste in clothes is dictated mainly by the composition of the fabric and how recently the material has been cleaned. It prefers natural fibres, especially if seasoned with a touch of sweat or urine, but the caterpillar can survive even on clean clothes, solely on the keratin contained in woollen fibres, although it develops slowly on this impoverished diet. It cannot digest artificial fibres but will quite happily munch its way around the less edible threads of composite fabrics.

In temperate regions, such as northern Europe, common clothes moths need the shelter of human houses to survive. Like many of the animals that have taken to sharing our lives, they have been able to exploit less favourable climatic regions by cohabiting with us. The clothes moth must have undergone a population explosion when houses began to be properly heated but it is now threatened by the increasing use of artificial fibres and the practice of impregnating wool with insecticides.

Carpet beetles, dustmites and clothes moths have been human nest companions since prehistoric times and when our ancestors left the cave to build shelters of their own they would have followed. As the early tent-like dwellings were often made from edible animal skins, the nest-dwellers would have eaten these too. Subsequently timber began to be incorporated into buildings, which attracted a horde of new and voracious invaders.

TIMBER!

EARLY BUILDINGS WERE CONSTRUCTED mainly of wood hewn from the forest and covered with a simple thatch of dried straw or leaves. These human homes were far from permanent. The forest already harboured animals and plants that specialised in consuming wood and, as there appeared to them little difference between a hut and a fallen tree, they quickly moved in.

Termites were among the first animals to attack our ancestors' shelters. These social insects cannot tackle such unpalatable food alone: they need the help of a specialised micro-organism. A colony of flagellates lives in the termite's gut and these single-celled creatures help to break down the indigestible cellulose in the wood. This partnership is essential – neither termite nor flagellate can survive alone.

Many termites inhabit subterranean nests close to buildings and make their surreptitious timber raids concealed in underground tunnels. Any dead wood is readily devoured and they find the enormous quantities assembled in human abodes irresistible.

Dry wood termites actually live inside the wood they consume. Their entire world may be no more than the interior of a single piece of furniture. As they devour their home, their only perception of the human sphere outside is through the dull vibrations created by our activity. Concealed from our view by a paper-thin veneer, they can, over several generations, hollow out a chair completely. These termites may then make a spectacular entrance

The first animals to attack human dwellings, termites consume more of the world's building timber than any other wood-eater.

into our world. A termite-ridden chair can disintegrate explosively in a cloud of dust as soon as someone sits down.

Such living hazards are confined to the warmer regions of the world as few termites survive in more temperate climes. The main timber-eaters of the cooler zones are wood-boring beetles. Unlike termites, only the larvae feed on wood. As they live solitary lives they only become noticed when their numbers build up over many years.

The woodworm that wreaks havoc in old furniture and wooden beams is the larval stage of the furniture beetle. It is so common that half of all British homes have these tiny maggot-like creatures munching away somewhere. The elongated brownish adults are smaller than a grain of rice and are rarely noticed as they scurry around, seeking a site to lay their eggs. They prefer rough, unpolished surfaces and their favourite spot is the underside of furniture. The eggs hatch after two to three weeks and the woodworm then spend the next three years slowly burrowing their way through the timber.

Throughout their literally boring lives, they remain concealed from human view. But they cannot escape enemies skilled in tracking them down. The mite pymotes rides piggy-back on the back of the woodworm and survives by sucking it dry. Parasitic wasps, attracted by the larva's odours, enter its burrow to lay eggs in its body. The wasp's young consume the woodworm alive. Some wasps can even pinpoint the hidden burrower through the wood surface. They achieve this impressive feat by sensing the vibrations created by their prey's rasping jaws. Then, using a syringe-like ovipositor, they skilfully penetrate the wood and inject a deadly dose of eggs. Woodworm that manage to avoid these fates create the characteristic exit holes when they emerge as adult beetles late in the summer.

Although furniture beetles still thrive in the dead wood of growing trees, they have considerably extended their natural range of habitation by moving in as our uninvited guests. Although the adults can fly, humans have created a more efficient method of dispersal in the form of removal vans.

The house longhorn beetle, which naturally lives in the sapwood of old pine trees, has even managed to emigrate by lodging with human beings. In its ancestral home of southern Europe this beetle likes it hot. In fact, the outside temperature has to reach a sultry 25 degrees Centigrade before the emerging adults can leave their wooden shelter. By infesting building timber they have used the protection of houses to spread northwards and have reached as far as the south of England.

Because of their impoverished diet, many wood-borers take a long time to reach maturity: it takes 30 years for the house longhorn beetle to emerge as an adult. Although they should therefore be renowned for their longevity, one of the most notorious of this type of insect has been traditionally associated with mortality.

The deathwatch beetle acquired its name through its eerie habit of tapping its head against a wooden beam. This ghostly head-banging, once believed to portend death, draws the male and female insects together. After mating, the beetle lays her cluster of around 50 eggs on decaying oak beams or other hardwood, often in churches or other old buildings. On hatching, the young spend some time searching for the perfect spot to begin their excavations, and then disappear inside the wood for up to 10 years. As the adults rarely fly, many existing colonies were introduced when the original timber was installed, and some of them must be several hundred years old.

The deathwatch beetle can create a stronghold only if fungi have already started the process of decay. Much of the destruction of building timber is aided by the actions of various of these moulds and mildews. Their spores, shed on the wind, shower down on every house.

THE ROT SETS IN

THE MICROSCOPIC SPORES OF fungi are light enough to be blown around
the world. Like miniature time capsules, they can remain in a state of
suspended animation for 40 years or more. Bombarded by a continual
blizzard of spores, even the cleanest homes cannot escape this fungal invasion.
For much of the time the spores are in continual motion, buoyed up on the
air currents created by our movements, but their aerial journey ends as soon
as they collide with a damp surface. A finger-like projection then issues from
the body of the spore and, if it makes contact with wood, starts to penetrate
it. As this hypha divides and then divides again it creates a ramifying web
of food-gathering mycelium that begins to digest the timber.

This invasive growth can only happen under damp conditions, so most
fungi thrive only where there is a regular supply of moisture from leaky roofs
or flaking paint surfaces. However, the dry rot fungus can survive in bone-
dry wood (which actually contains 20 per cent water). Once established, it
has the uncanny ability to invade even drier beams by piping up water from
the original timber. Its tendrils may cross several metres of barren bricks and
masonry as they search for fresh wood. Once they have located a good source
of food, a bracket-like fruiting body, up to a metre across, erupts from the
web of mycelium. This gives rise to literally millions of tiny spores, which
float on the slightest current of air and drift away to invade new premises.
More than any other fungus, dry rot is perfectly adapted to the domestic life
and, although it must have originated in the forest, it is now found only in
human company.

With so many organisms capable of devouring wooden buildings almost
as soon as they were built, few traces remain of the first human dwellings.
As the early hunter-gatherers lived a nomadic existence, the ephemeral
nature of their shelters hardly mattered to them. Even today, people who
continue this way of life still abandon their homes when too many uninvited
lodgers move in.

When people began to grow crops, 10 000 years ago, moving house
became less convenient and these early farmers made a radical improvement,
incorporating stone into their buildings to render them more durable.

A HOUSE OF STONE

FLOCKS OF PIGEONS THAT today fly along the Nile valley are descendants
of birds that associated with the new farmers as agriculture swept through
the Middle East and North Africa. The birds' eyes contain coloured filters,
made of red and orange oil droplets, that are believed to enhance the

Pigeons still thrive on the Pyramid of Zozer – the oldest stone monument in the world.

variation seen in green vegetation. This helps them locate lush feeding grounds and, in the past, the crops of the early agriculturalists must have proved irresistible to them. Originally birds of the sea-cliffs, they found the artificial cliffs formed by the farmers' buildings perfect substitutes for their natural nest-sites.

A colony is still living on the 4700-year-old Pyramid of Zozer in Saqqara, Egypt – the oldest stone monument in the world. As pigeons are known to use man-made structures as navigation landmarks, these birds must be familiar with many of the temples and lesser pyramids that surround the site. By detecting infrasounds, which are pitched below human hearing, they will also be aware of noises emanating from Cairo nearly 30 kilometres away. This city's eclectic jumble of buildings demonstrates the diversity of styles and designs that people have created over time, ranging from humble stone dwellings to the Nile Hilton. Pigeons have been able to adapt to many of them.

Man-made rock-faces also attract other birds, such as the house martin. These originally built their dome-like nests under the overhangs created by horizontal fractures on sea-cliffs and rocks. The eaves of houses mirrored these natural nest-sites and the birds soon came to prefer them, as they were less exposed. As lodgers on human homes they were able to multiply rapidly

The artificial caves created by buildings proved irresistible to swallows. By moving in with humans they have increased their populations and spread to new areas.

and spread across Europe. Today they even manage to breed in the Arctic Circle.

The new stone buildings also benefited many of the creatures that had shared the lives of our cave-dwelling ancestors. At Cresswell Crags, near Sheffield, caves that once protected neolithic people still shelter nesting swallows. Such birds are now a rarity as, like their human companions, the majority have abandoned the caves. They now build their cup-shaped nests of mud and saliva on the artificial ledges of buildings. This change of habit took place several thousand years ago and by Greek and Roman times the swallow's aerial acrobatics were a familiar feature of villa life.

The swallows that swooped and swerved around the Grecian rooftops viewed the buildings not only as luxury caverns but also as a reliable source of food. Human dwellings attracted swarms of flies and other insects and today swallows continue to gather a harvest in mid-air around farm buildings and outhouses. They also find ideal nest-sites on ledges and beams under overhanging roofs. In such ideal conditions they will rear two or three broods in a season.

Although the adults return to the same nest-sites each year, their off-spring usually colonise new breeding locations. To ensure they can find these chosen nest-sites again, before they migrate the young swallows make many reconnoitring flights to familiarise themselves with the local area. This house-hunting habit must have accelerated their invasion into the first stone dwellings. Today they are no longer rare birds, restricted by the scarcity of caves, but one of the most widespread in Europe.

BIRD ARCHITECTS

MANY TYPES OF SWIFTS have also profited from the expansion of housing. Even nest-builders with the most esoteric requirements found a niche among the great range of architectural styles on offer. The alpine, pallid and white-rumped swifts found substitute rock-crevices under the roofs of buildings. Instead of a cave or overhanging rock, the house swift could sling its bag-shaped nest from under the eaves of houses or in the cavernous interiors of mosques. Over most of Europe the common swift found the space between the eaves and the wall a perfect replacement for rotten holes in old trees. Because it feeds on aerial plankton, such as spiders and aphids, sucked up to a high altitude in the vortex of thermals, it is less affected by city pollution

White storks have profited from the spread of agriculture.
A chimney acts as a sturdy substitute for the crown of a tree.

than other swifts and swallows and will nest further into town centres.

Spine-tailed swifts found their desirable residences in the shape of chimneys. These mimic the boles of decayed trees and, when much of the primal forest of the United States was cleared for agriculture, the chimney swift was quick to find alternative housing. Large factory chimneys, which act as outsized tree-trunks, can attract as many as 10 000 roosting birds.

Chimneys appeal to many other tree-hole nesters. Starlings take over small ones, while slightly larger versions attract jackdaws. As the spread of agriculture cleared vast tracts of forest, these birds reaped their own harvest.

The white stork was another beneficiary, finding the new meadows, arable fields and pastures an ideal source of insects, frogs and small mammals. Tolerated and often encouraged by the farmers, it began to nest on their buildings, discovering that chimneys and rooftops could support its huge construction of branches and twigs as effectively as the crown of a tree.

HOUSE HUNTERS

NOT ONLY BIRDS HAVE adapted to life on our buildings. In the warmer regions of the world several species of rock-dwelling lizards colonise artificial stonework. Their bulbous eyes are adapted to nocturnal vision and, in apparently total darkness, they gaze down on their human companions as though watching through image-intensifiers. Their stare, which to us appears disturbingly unbroken, is the result of having no eyelids. Instead, they periodically wipe their eyes clean by using their mobile tongue as a windscreen wiper.

A hunting gecko ignores the irrelevant human activity that may continue below and instead watches for the movement of any small insect. It will boldly cross exposed walls and ceilings to find its prey and in its race for food the gecko may scurry along ceilings and even up window glass. It defies gravity by using toes that are expanded into flattened cushions and covered with microscopic hook-cells. The hooks act like miniature Velcro and engage in the slightest surface irregularity.

Geckoes quickly learn that they can hunt more efficiently if they position themselves around electric lights. These act as artificial lures which confuse the navigation systems of flying insects. The gecko simply pounces on the confetti of disorientated insects that flutter towards it.

One of the few vocal reptiles, geckoes use their calls to find each other through the labyrinth of our dwellings. The giant Asian tokay, nearly half a metre in length, is the most impressive vocalist, with a staccato bark that competes with that of a dog. Because of their expertise at controlling insects these noisy companions are still welcomed in most houses.

Geckoes have also moved in as lodgers. Electric lights act as lures to draw in flying insects.

Like many house-dwellers the gecko's domestic lifestyle allowed it to move into new areas. The common gecko originated in North Africa but ships transported it to the South of France, the Canary Islands and a few South Pacific islands. The Turkish gecko, once confined to the Mediterranean and Red Sea coasts, has now reached South America. Other house geckoes have indulged in similar globe-trotting.

As geckoes hunt around the lights of human dwellings they are often accompanied by bats. Usually these seek the same insect prey but the false vampire actually preys upon the geckoes.

BATS IN THE BELFRY

BATS HAVE BEEN ASSOCIATED with human homes throughout history and they too shared the caves of our ancestors. They scrutinise our modern living quarters by calling out and listening for the echoes that bounce off the walls. Like a human shouting in a cathedral, the bat can gain a sense of distance from the time it takes an echo to return. But the bat shouts in a falsetto pitched seven octaves higher than a human soprano and may make 200 calls every second. From the returning reverberations it gains enough information to construct a picture in sound. It uses this echolocation not only to find its insect food but also a place to live. To a bat's sonar there is little difference between natural sites and the replicas created in human abodes.

Cave-dwelling bats find that tombs, crypts, cellars and other stone and brick structures offer equally suitable shelter. Bats that naturally squeeze into rock fissures discover similar crevices under tiles or corrugated roofs and behind wooden shutters. The inhabitants of rotten tree cavities find the same living quarters in the interiors of cavity walls, floor spaces, attics and barns.

These substitute sites may be used for breeding, roosting or hibernation, and some bats commute between artificial and natural locations as their requirements change. Most species are sensitive to extremes of temperature but some tropical free-tailed bats have been known to shelter under corrugated iron roofs at a scorching 50 degrees Centigrade.

Over the last few centuries, as natural sites were destroyed, buildings became increasingly favoured. This change of habit allowed many bats to spread into new areas. In Norway and Sweden, bats, using buildings as ersatz homes, now survive above the tree-line and exploit the insect glut of the short northern summer. In Panama the formerly scarce black myotis bat has been able to increase its population and region of habitation by adapting to purely man-made sites. The same has happened in North America with the big brown bat and the little brown bat.

A variety of animal lodgers profited from the spread of buildings. As human numbers expanded, another group was able to benefit from the vast quantities of waste that these growing villages and towns created.

METROPOLITAN SCAVENGERS

IN THE CITY OF Addis Ababa, Ethiopia, participants from the primeval hunter and scavenger drama played out on the East African savannah are now attracted to modern leftovers. As the light dims, the streets are filled with the shadowy shapes of hyenas making their way towards the city dump. The mirror-like retinas in their eyes, designed to gather the slightest glimmer, reflect the lights of human dwellings as they once glinted by primal campfires.

At dawn the hyenas are joined by vultures, which monitor the movements of people from far above villages and cities. The waste from slaughterhouses and rubbish tips provides substantially richer pickings than predator kills.

Black kites have also taken to a metropolitan way of life across the African and Asian continents. Like vultures, their eyesight is acute, with telephoto capacity. As the kites float over the city streets they scan for signs of human activity that indicate a free meal. Their swooping talons scoop up any discarded scraps of food, such as offal from butcher's shops, which are eaten on the wing.

Like this dwarf bat, many bats have taken to a life in human dwellings. This change in their behaviour has allowed some species to colonise areas that were previously uninhabitable for them.

Kites were once common in medieval London, where they were so highly valued as refuse collectors it was made a capital offence to kill one. As waste disposal became more efficient, the kites disappeared, but today cities like London sustain a new generation of scavenger.

CITY SLICKERS

INITIALLY THE SPREAD OF human habitation was ribbon-like, hugging the new roads that fed the expanding towns but leaving reserves of country-side or parkland between. Eventually these green spaces began to infill with housing, trapping the resident wildlife inside. Although many of these animals had previously avoided contact with people, the residential invasion took place gradually and a number could adapt. They were helped by changes in the way waste was discarded. In many countries it was now left in bins outside individual houses. Diverse scavenging mammals began to discover the advantages of this packaged food.

Throughout Europe and North America the red fox took to city life and even in Australia the introduced fox population developed its own breed of town-dwellers. The highest numbers of urban foxes are now found in Britain and in many cities they reach higher densities than in the surrounding countryside. As many as two fox families may exist in a single square kilometre, a density twice as high as the best rural areas and two hundred times higher than on some upland moorlands. In fact more foxes now live in London than in the whole of the rural South-east of England.

These urbanites are usually tolerated by the human population and their only real enemy is the automobile. Brought up entirely in the town, they regard this noisy world as their native home and the concrete of pavements and roads as natural as trees or grass. Foraging is actually easier than in country areas. Lawns and gardens provide an endless supply of worms, birds, small mammals and insects, and foxes can supplement their diet with food gleaned from rubbish bins.

The fox's success is helped by its catholic tastes in food. Once it developed a penchant for city dining it moved further into the heart of the metropolis. Foxes now forage in the streets of Central London, and in New York City they have even reached Central Park and the Bronx. On the outskirts of some American cities they are joined on their garbage can missions by grey foxes and a host of other scavenging mammals.

Black kites reconnoitre above the streets of towns and cities in
Africa and Asia in the same way as they once followed the
activities of early humans.

NIGHT RAIDERS

IN LOS ANGELES, CALIFORNIA, the hum of the night traffic now competes with the howl of the urban coyote. During daylight hours these wolf-like carnivores shelter in the scrub-filled ravines that section the hillside developments. At night they leave to raid the more built-up areas, crossing busy freeways and even visiting fast-food joints in their search for discarded snacks.

The city streets have become part of their accepted environment and they even use them for hunting, finding substitutes for their natural quarry among household pets such as cats and rabbits. They will kill small dogs, such as poodles. Larger dogs receive a friendlier reception: like the wolf, the coyote is a close relative of the dog and the two will readily crossbreed.

Raccoons, though less aggressive urban raiders, have also adapted to town life remarkably well. They now prowl the backstreets of most American cities and reach their greatest numbers in Washington DC. Their success is due partly to their omnivorous appetites, but in addition they are agile climbers and will readily scale walls and fences to pilfer the contents of a rubbish bin. Sometimes they carry out brazen sorties into houses to steal food from kitchens.

Their dexterous front paws make them nimble burglars, as they use them to lift doorlatches, turn doorknobs and even open the doors of fridges. Once inside, raccoons are not deterred by modern packaging as they readily learn to unscrew the caps of jars, bottles and other containers. Those that have acquired the knack of pulling corks from restoppered wine bottles sometimes stagger from the house in an inebriated state.

On these nocturnal wanderings the raccoon may sometimes encounter a foraging skunk. These have acquired a similar taste for the contents of the garbage can, and such meetings may result in the skunk raising its tail and spraying the acrid contents of its anal glands at the rival marauder. The skunk's pelt is emblazoned with bold black and white markings to warn other animals of this hidden chemical weapon. This makes the skunk the most conspicuous of all urban scavengers and guarantees that it is left alone.

SUBURBAN LIFESTYLES

TWO EUROPEAN RELATIVES OF THE skunk have also discovered the nutritional value of human food. In Britain, the spread of housing has encroached on the territories of badgers, bringing this new and guaranteed supply of provisions within reach.

Their sets, possibly several hundred years old, are usually built in steeply sloping banks which are often unsuitable for housing construction. In some

*In Germany the cavities of car engines provide temporary refuge
for inquisitive stone-martens.*

new suburban sites these ancient sets, and their inhabitants, may become
completely surrounded by modern houses and the badgers manage to survive
by searching gardens and dustbins for something to eat.

In Germany, Switzerland and Austria, the urbanisation of vast tracts
of countryside has similarly invaded the living space of stone-martens. Unlike
the badger, these ferret-like animals naturally have no fixed abode and could
readily adapt their gypsy lives to the streets. Like agoraphobic people, they
feel insecure in open spaces but have discovered that the engine com-
partments of cars provide a secure refuge. Audis, BMWs and Mercedes are
regularly invaded by stone-martens and the cars are often immobilised as
these inquisitive creatures chew through the wiring and rubber engine parts.
The damage reaches a peak around the breeding season when the female
uses the engine space as a nursery for her cubs.

MANIPULATIVE MACAQUES

IN INDIA RHESUS MACAQUE monkeys have taken to urban life and acquired many of the attributes of human city-dwellers, among them a cunning nature.

Each morning, as dawn breaks through the haze over the rooftops of Varanasi, monkeys demonstrate their slyness in acquiring food. They watch for people spreading washing out on the roofs to dry. Having learnt that clothes can be used for extortion, as soon as the people leave, they pounce. Their preference is for brightly coloured items, if possible with lots of buttons. When they have made their choice, they sit down and provocatively remove each button with their teeth.

If the garment's owner attempts to scare the monkey, it simply runs off with its trophy. A better plan is to distract the animal by throwing food: as it runs to seize the placatory gift, the clothes can then be retrieved. This blackmail routine probably started accidentally but now the monkeys deliberately use it to procure a meal.

Tolerated because of their association with the monkey god, Hanuman, the macaques make their rascally presence felt in many other Indian cities, often raiding markets or entering houses to steal food. In Delhi, they have made the Institute of Medical Sciences their favourite haunt and patients have been known to emerge from the anaesthetic to discover a monkey sharing their bed or fiddling with their drips.

Of all the mammals that have adopted a city existence the monkeys are the most resourceful. Perhaps because of their similarity to humans they have readily accepted the changes associated with urban living. In the countryside they seek a new sleeping place each night but in town they always return to the same base. They also enjoy human food in preference to a more natural diet. But, like humans living in cities, these macaques tend to show more aggression and stress than their country cousins.

The cities that now contain the highest densities of humans, and often the biggest social problems, are home to the least wildlife. But in the hearts of even the most modern cities a few animal specialists still manage to survive.

MIAMI VULTURES

THE ART DECO ROOF of City Hall in Miami is now embellished with living decorations. Turkey vultures have made the building their home and they use it as a vantage point to survey the city. Like African vultures, they utilise rising currents of warm air to lift them upwards. This happens each morning as the sun begins to bake the parking lots below. The turkey vultures take

*In India streetwise macaques have taken on many of the habits
of human city-dwellers.*

off and drift over the skyscrapers of downtown Miami, seeking the scraps left
over from modern meals.

Their technique is different from that of Old World vultures. Instead of
using vision they rely on their acute sense of smell to guide them to food.
Turkey vultures can locate a freshly killed mammal hidden in dense scrub
from a distance of several kilometres, but these city vultures rarely face such
challenges. Invariably their highly developed nostrils direct them to the
municipal dump. Here they are joined by cattle egrets, starlings, grackles
and red-wing blackbirds. Together they sift through human cast-offs to find
edible morsels. Squawking over their heads and plucking morsels of food
from the jaws of bulldozers are myriads of gulls.

Gulls have changed their sea-faring lifestyle to feed on the waste products of modern lives.

GARBAGE GULLS

BIRDS THAT ONCE FORAGED only at sea or along the shoreline have changed their behaviour to exploit the detritus of contemporary lives. Garbage-loving gulls are now common throughout North America and Europe. But it took a while before the habit became established. First the birds had to learn that this puzzling assortment of debris contained edible ingredients.

Young gulls still have problems identifying food. They discover what litter is safe to eat by watching more experienced birds and often resort to stealing from adults to obtain a meal. It takes four years for them to acquire enough knowledge of human waste to compete successfully with other gulls.

As gulls take time to gain this expertise there was initially a delay before a rubbish tip culture became established. But now that several species of gull depend on it, it has not only altered their feeding habits, but has also influenced their migration patterns and the size of their populations. Lesser black-backed gulls, once summer visitors, now overwinter in Britain to take advantage of this guaranteed food supply. Until recently the numbers of British herring gulls, sustained by food foraged from tips, were increasing at a rate of nearly 15 per cent each year.

Like many other birds, pied wagtails have discovered the heating benefits of urban roosting.

With the gulls' population rising at this phenomenal rate, it was inevitable that traditional breeding sites on cliffs suffered the stress of overcrowding. The ousted birds sought out alternative ledges and found them on the artificial stacks created by buildings. Ironically, it was in crowded human towns that the gulls found a peaceful haven. Here nesting birds had fewer problems with neighbours and could rear their young successfully.

Although gulls avoid the barren cliffs and rock-faces of city centres, many other birds travel great distances just to spend the night on the desolate ledges of these canyons.

A NIGHT ON THE TOWN

SHORTLY BEFORE DUSK, ENORMOUS flocks of dancing, spiralling starlings weave their way towards the hearts of many of our most populated cities. The various constructions offer ideal sites for roosting birds, generating warmth and sheltering them from the wind. On calm, clear nights the temperature difference between the centre of town and the surrounding countryside can be as much as 2–3 degrees Centigrade. Close to buildings it may be even greater because of escaping heat and trapped air.

Today peregrines hunt their traditional pigeon prey in the urban canyons of New York. Their population is now at the maximum the city will sustain.

The habit of roosting in these heat-traps began to develop at the turn of the century and since then the number of urban roosts has grown steadily. In Britain, most cities and large towns have at least one starling roost and some of the larger conurbations, such as Newcastle, have several, with populations in excess of 50 000 birds. Across the rest of Europe many of the major cities now act as starling dormitories and these sleeping habits have also been adopted among the starlings introduced to North America and Australia.

In parts of Europe, such as Sweden, Finland and Bulgaria, jackdaws roost in towns, and in winter the whole population within a 35 kilometre radius may converge for this purpose on favoured urban sites. Birds foraging furthest from the city actually use more energy flying to the roost than they gain from the shelter it provides, but as the flight lines to and from roosts also give useful information about the location of new feeding grounds, the jackdaws still benefit from the journey.

As well as cosiness these city bolt holes provide some protection from predators. However, several birds of prey have adopted the urban life and these will swoop through the circling flocks as they assemble for the night.

URBAN GUERRILLAS

IN EUROPEAN CITIES THE main predator at starling roosts is the sparrow hawk, but in both Europe and North America peregrine falcons may also be attracted. The peregrine even hunts in the centre of New York City. For this cliff-nester, the buildings create irresistible ravines, with nesting spots and high vantage points from which victims can be pinpointed. The peregrine relies on speed to catch prey, sweeping back its wings to form a sickle that slices through the air at over 100 miles an hour.

That this ancient aerial battle is possible in the heart of overcrowded cities shows just how versatile life is at exploiting even the most altered landscapes. These few opportunist animals have found ways of benefiting from increasing human populations – often in the absence of our encouragement or awareness.

The urban peregrine moved into town following its prey of starlings or pigeons. These flock birds began to associate with people as agriculture started to change human lives. The partnership that developed between people and plants had a profound effect on our relationships with animals, not only those that scavenged from us or lived in our homes but also those that thrived on our crops.

*In the Kalahari desert, Bushmen still continue the gathering
way of life of our ancestors.*

CHAPTER
2

SEEDS OF LIFE

I N T H E F O R E S T S O F South America a form of intensive agri-culture has been practised for millions of years. The cultivation is so widespread that few plants remain untouched by it, yet this highly developed activity is pursued in complete harmony with the environment. The ecologically minded farmers are leaf-cutting ants.

Crisscrossing the forest floor, countless lines of these ants follow chemical trails that take them to their favoured source of compost. From leaves their razor-sharp jaws slice disc shapes, which they raise above their heads and, like a flag-waving procession, carry back to their underground nest. The leafy banners are then shredded and buried.

The ants, following the principles of good husbandry, are preparing the soil for their crops. They grow mushrooms. Not the variety familiar to humans but a distantly related type of fungus whose survival requires far more rigorously controlled conditions. The ants not only provide the perfect compost, but also maintain ideal temperature and humidity levels. Their techniques are sophisticated: they apply chemicals to keep down the growth of bacteria and transplant fungus cuttings from well-established cultivated plots in order to create new allotments.

On these foraging expeditions the leaf-cutters frequently encounter the crops of human farmers and eagerly harvest the leaves. Compared with the ancient heritage of the ants, human agriculture is a relatively recent development, having emerged only 10 000 years ago. Its spread around the globe since that time has had radical repercussions on both the nature and balance of plant life and also the numbers and dispersal of animals – including people.

Until the advent of agriculture, wild plants were simply gathered by humans, who made little attempt to influence their growth. Even so, just by selecting which to eat and discarding the seeds, these early people had an effect on the local plant population. It was from such casual beginnings that agriculture first took off.

GATHERING SEED

IN THE KALAHARI DESERT in southern Africa, Bushmen maintain this original relationship between people and plants. The plants that the Bushmen gather for food have evolved to have some control over their own fate. Many defend themselves with thorns and stings or their leaves contain cellulose, which humans find indigestible. Those that contain poisons often have a bitter taste as a warning of the danger. The Bushmen know by experience which to avoid and which can be made palatable by special preparation.

In contrast, some plants use succulent fruits to entice birds and mammals (Bushmen included) to consume them. Melons, common in the region, prove particularly tempting. Once the flesh has been eaten, the Bushmen spit out the seeds, often far from the parent plant. In this way the plants succeed in dispersing their seeds.

Certain fruits, such as the berries of the Grewia bush, found in the Kalahari, actually require their seeds to be eaten. The seeds are dispersed only after surviving the hazardous journey through the body. Some seeds can only germinate once their outer coat has been digested. Other types need to leave the body quickly to avoid being digested, so contain a laxative to help speed their passage. Figs are a good example of the second kind, and a renowned cure for constipation for this very reason.

Seeds swallowed by the Bushmen end up on a latrine near the village. This area, richly fertilised and cleared of competing vegetation, offers the perfect conditions for germination. Each human visit to the latrine sends out olfactory signals to iridescent dung beetles, which arrive within seconds and immediately begin to dig out a nest chamber. As they burrow, they bury the seeds. As a result of this fortuitous planting, old deserted village sites are often surrounded by the Bushmen's favourite food plants. After a period of years have elapsed new villages are built close to these unintentional crops.

The relationship between people and plants remained at this casual level for most of human existence. The plants often gained from the relationship as humans helped disperse the seeds and the gatherers were able to harvest the crops they had accidentally sown.

For the people involved this way of life was far from arduous. In the apparently barren wastes of the Kalahari desert, a woman takes only six hours to gather enough food to feed a family for three days. Although this food is supplemented with meat caught by the men, the bulk of the diet comes from the gathered plants. The Bushmen's natural larder consists of 84 different vegetables, expanded in the rainy season by a choice array of fruits.

The Bushmen show that, even in a desert, the gathering way of life is relatively easy. It not only offers a wide variety of food but also allows plenty

*For the Bushmen, gathering is far from arduous. Even in the
desert a woman can gather enough food in six hours to feed a
family for three days.*

of spare time for other activity. Once, everyone obtained their food in this
fashion. But, if this existence was so comfortable, why did people give it up
in favour of cultivating plants?

It seems that the decision was not a conscious one. The relationship
already formed with a handful of gathered plants gradually strengthened
and cultivation was the eventual and inevitable consequence. The first
steps in this direction were accidental and the plants themselves played an
important role in the transition.

STAFF OF LIFE

IN THE MIDDLE EAST of 10 000 years ago, the wild grasses of the region
were about to transform the lives of the people that gathered them. These
grasses, forms of wheat known as einkorn and emmer, still grow profusely on
the foothills of mountains that curve around the north of the Arabian desert.
This 'Fertile Crescent' arcs through the countries now called Iran, Iraq,
Turkey, Syria, Israel and Jordan. The humans who had begun to gather the

seeds of these grasses discovered that, over the period of ripening, they could gather enough grain to last them for the rest of the year.

They settled close to these prolific wild stands of einkorn and emmer and, although they did not deliberately cultivate them, they came to rely on the success of the yearly harvest. They had unwittingly started a relationship that would ultimately cause them to leave the easy gathering life behind.

To ensure a productive harvest they were forced to spend an increasing amount of time protecting the plants from both animal and other human competitors. As harvest time approached, their problems intensified. Birds, such as sparrows, would migrate into the area to gorge themselves on the ripening seeds. As they alighted, the fragile ears of any ripe wheat would break and their seeds, shaped like aerodynamic darts, were propelled into the ground. Any that failed to bury themselves would be eaten by mice. When people tried to harvest the crop the seed head shattered in a similar way and made the seed difficult to gather.

But some of these plants had a feature that made gathering easier: they had ears that, when ripe, stayed intact. People would gather more seeds from these types of grasses, which would then either be planted deliberately or grow up on the sites of old threshing grounds. The offspring of these plants would have retained this nonshattering characteristic. Over many seasons, this unwitting selection of easily harvested varieties caused a speeded up form of evolution. Eventually, what developed was a type of wheat that no longer shed its seeds of its own accord but needed to be harvested by human hands.

The new wheats now relied on people to propagate them, but people depended equally on the wheats for their own survival. Nourished by the new crop, their villages were growing in size and the expanding populations could thrive only if the harvest was successful.

These humans had left the relatively undemanding life of hunter-gatherers behind and become locked in an alliance with a plant. For these early farmers there was no going back. Their populations had grown so large they could no longer be supported simply by gathering. They now had to tend their crops continually to ensure enough food to go round: the amount of labour required was greater than if they had continued as they were.

Throughout the Fertile Crescent many different groups of people became locked into this type of partnership and plants other than wheat began to benefit from the care bestowed upon them. Barley became cultivated during the same period and it too lost the ability to shed its seeds.

In this pact between people and plants both sides profited by expanding their populations and spreading to new areas, but they had become totally reliant on each other. The humans now faced competition from interloping species that had found ways of sneaking into the alliance.

Wheat began its association with people in the Fertile Crescent
of the Middle East around 10 000 years ago.

AGAINST THE GRAIN

FLOCKS OF SPARROWS WOVE above the people toiling in the wheat fields, just as they once joined the gatherers of wild grain. The birds even stopped migrating away after the harvest as, by feeding from the farmers' foodstores, they could now stay throughout the year. Conveniently, human dwellings provided the perfect nest-sites. The sparrow had become the house sparrow and, through this association with people, it spread wherever agriculture developed and eventually colonised much of the world.

The mouse that gathered the spilt grain of the wild grasses also moved in alongside the new farmers, readily adapting to an existence among humans and turning into the house mouse. The lives of these first foodstore pests are now so entwined with those of humans that they can be found throughout the inhabited world, including the polar regions.

People often become aware of the presence of the house mouse when

The sparrow was the first animal to profit from the new partnership between people and grain. Sparrow flocks grew quickly as the first civilisations developed.

they notice the sweet, musty smell it leaves behind. This is the pungent residue of the mouse's aromatic conversations. Mice live in a world governed by odours and the same scent signals that once controlled the lives of mice in the wild grasslands can pervade houses today.

Under the floorboards a dominant male mouse influences his extended family by leaving fragrant signals on scent posts spread throughout his home. The smells warn off competing males and even cause young males to delay reaching puberty. The effect on females is equally dramatic. The odour can speed the onset of puberty by as much as 20 days and, if it reaches a pregnant female from another group, her embryos may be reabsorbed or even aborted. In this way the male maintains the integrity of the mouse population and keeps it under his control.

However, the first civilisations, fed by the few favoured plants of agriculture, were not plagued only by animal interlopers such as the house sparrow and the house mouse (7000 years ago a major problem in the expanding granaries of Ancient Egypt). They were also vulnerable to failures in the crop caused by other organisms beating humans to the harvest.

*The house mouse was an early invader of food stores, a change
of habit that allowed it to spread across the whole world.*

MARAUDING HORDES

AN INSIGNIFICANT SHORT-HORNED grasshopper was on occasion able
to devastate the early human civilisations. For most of the time this insect
lives far from human habitation, existing on the scrub of the desert. But
periodically, under particular conditions of overcrowding, the grasshoppers
experience a transformation. They grow membranous wings and develop a
restless and gregarious nature. Eventually locust swarms many million strong
take off in a fearsome migration.

In the air they space out to avoid collision but a single square kilometre
may contain 150 million individual insects, while some swarms are so vast
that their numbers reach an astronomical 40 000 million. Travelling at 15
kilometres an hour, they can fly for up to five days and, helped by wind,
have even been known to cross the Atlantic. Usually their journeys are
confined to northern Africa, with the main thrust of the migration encircling
the Sahara desert. Prevailing winds take them to areas of high rainfall.

When flying into a wind the vast invertebrate air force hugs the ground to reduce exposure to air turbulence, but if the wind is in the preferred direction the swarms rise up, to heights of over 3000 metres, in huge apocalyptic clouds. As the locusts fly, the leading edge will peel away to descend on any vegetation in their path. The damage they wreak has its full impact on humans when this rolling cloud passes over crops.

To the early Egyptian civilisation the destruction could be catastrophic. A relatively small swarm may contain 50 million locusts and in a single day they can eat food that would sustain 500 people for a year. The largest swarms can consume a gargantuan 80 000 tonnes a day, the equivalent of the annual needs of 400 000 humans.

But the crop could be devastated by animals not only while it was growing. If people were to survive beyond the harvest period they had to store the produce and this attracted a whole new range of opportunists.

CUPBOARD LOVE

LIVING ALONGSIDE THE LOCUST in the scorching deserts stretching from the Sahara to Iran is a related insect, the cricket. This general scavenger must have joined the mouse in attacking the Egyptian foodstores, but it was confined to the warmer parts of the world until artificially heated homes and buildings recreated a desert climate in temperate lands.

Bakeries and kitchens were favoured targets as were private houses with continually burning hearth fires. Only the warmest locations were chosen and frequently, between the loose bricks of the hearth-side or bread oven, the cricket found arid conditions similar to those in its ancestral home. The house cricket finally reached Britain in the sixteenth century and became one of the few scavengers to be welcomed by their human hosts. The chirruping of the cricket, a sexual signal created by the rubbing of legs on wing-cases, was associated with the cosiness of a warm hearth, and the crickets were often left to multiply undisturbed.

The tombs of Egyptian pharaohs who died as long as 4500 years ago contain traces of other pioneering insect opportunists. Flour beetles thrived in the ancient granaries, just as today they raid flour and cereal stores throughout the world. Like house crickets, they need the artificial warmth provided by buildings to survive in cooler climes.

The reddish-brown drugstore or biscuit beetle also gorged itself on the foodstores of the Egyptians and it infiltrates household larders today. This insect too prefers grain products such as bread and flour but it will survive on any stored food, including meat, soup powders and spices. It readily

*Above: As soon as people began to store food they attracted a host
of insect invaders. This beetle has infested a store of mung beans.
Below: The house cricket found the desert conditions
of its ancestral home reproduced around European
hearth fires. It survives on scraps of bread and
other food.*

burrows through books and manuscripts and even has a taste for poisonous materials such as belladonna and strychnine, which it can consume with no apparent harm.

Spider beetles were yet more uninvited guests at the early feast and, as grain-based agriculture spread, flour mites, mealworm beetles and grain weevils joined the growing fraternity of grain-feeding animals.

With so many animals consuming either the growing crop or the stored grain the agricultural way of life was proving far from effortless. But the people who adopted it were able to increase their populations and cultivation began to spread across Europe.

CEREAL CHANGE

TAKEN FAR FROM ITS warm ancestral home, wheat had to change if it was to survive as a crop of the northern farmers. A happy accident took care of this. As the wheat was planted in the north it encountered local grasses that were already adapted to the local climate. They interbred, the cross creating a hardier wheat. The new variety contained the protein gluten, which allowed the bread to be leavened, and the grain was no longer enclosed in a husk, which made threshing easier. The farmers did not set out deliberately to modify wheat, but the strains with characteristics most attractive to their cultivators obviously tended to thrive.

As wheat evolved it became totally dependent on human protection for its survival. Even if it had been capable of shedding its seeds itself, they would not have been able to compete with other plants. It was only because of the yearly ploughing of fields and sowing of seeds by humans that the stands of wheat were prevented from being smothered by more vigorous competitors.

WEEDING OUT

ALTHOUGH PLOUGHING KEPT DOWN perennial plants, some species were able to prosper and an array of opportunist weeds, such as the cornflower, corncockle, corn marigold and field pansy, flourished in the crop. Some, like charlock, which turns fields a vivid yellow, are now virtually extinct away from cultivated land.

Many weeds were plants that had thrived after the glaciers of the last ice age retreated, but were pushed out as the vegetation returned. They

Previous pages: Poppies rely on chance disturbances of the soil to promote germination. Ploughing caused these previously freak events to happen once a year.

found that the new fields created favourable conditions once more. Poppies, which can lie dormant as seeds for over a hundred years and rely on chance disturbances to the soil to promote germination, discovered that these once freak events occurred each year as the plough passed by.

Among the weeds of these European fields were other varieties of grass. One of these produced nutritious grains that nodded pendulously from an array of bending stems. This plant was tolerated in the crop and in cool, moist, maritime regions it fared even better than the wheat. Eventually it stopped being regarded as a weed and began to be grown for its own sake. Another partnership had been born: this time between people and oats. Like wheat, oats benefited from becoming commonly cultivated.

The spread of cereals across Europe not only nourished the growth of human populations. As agriculture reached fresh areas it met new animal opportunists. One of the most successful of these had originally associated with people when the human race first emerged in Africa, but it was only able to mount a global invasion once agriculture became widespread.

ENCROACHING COCKROACHES

TODAY, IN AFRICA'S KALAHARI DESERT, the Bushmen's discarded food is often consumed by cockroaches. These shiny brown insects, with their long, waving antennae, must have scurried around emerging homo sapiens in the Great Rift valley. In fact, all the cockroaches that have invaded the modern world originate from Africa.

They raid kitchens under the cover of darkness, sneaking out of cracks and similar hiding places to search for edible fragments. Their universe is perceived mainly through taste sensors located in their mouth-parts. Sampling a single molecule is sufficient for them to distinguish between food and poison. In fact, they reject very little: the secret of the cockroach's phenomenal success lies partly in its capacity to eat almost anything. Cockroaches also excel at overcoming the clumsy attempts of their hosts to kill them. These encounters often take place when the insects' nocturnal feasting is disturbed by a human seeking a midnight snack.

Cockroaches watch their human companions through compound eyes containing a limited number of facets, so they perceive only broad areas of light and shade. However, they are extremely sensitive to changes in light level and dart away the instant a light is turned on.

Those caught out in the open rely on a special sense to protect them. Two finger-like organs known as cerci project from the back of the cockroach and these are covered by fine sensory hairs that react to moving air molecules. Sound waves or the minutest murmur of air cause these sensitive hairs to

shimmer. They can even respond to the footfalls of another cockroach so the pressure wave from a descending human foot must appear to them like a gale warning. The cockroach responds to such danger five times faster than human reflexes and beetles off before the lumbering foot strikes home.

The cockroach's superior reflexes have helped it outmanoeuvre people for centuries. But it needed more than quick reactions to survive outside the tropics. Without the artificial climate provided by human buildings, the cockroach would still be confined to the equatorial zones.

Their spread, which has taken them far from their original homelands, started as soon as global trade began to break down geographical barriers and maritime routes linked up the different agricultural regions of the world.

The names given to types of cockroach fail to reflect their African origins. The Oriental cockroach was carried by early trading vessels to the eastern Mediterranean and from there it spread northwards and westwards. It reached South America on Spanish ships and burgeoning ocean trade dispersed it around the world. It is now found in virtually all regions of North America and is the most familiar cockroach in Britain.

The histories of other cockroaches are similarly linked to the vagaries of world trade. The American cockroach was transported from tropical Africa to the United States on slave ships and it went on to become the commonest cockroach in the world. The German cockroach was confined to Ethiopia and the Sudan until Greek and Phoenician ships carried it through Turkey to the Black Sea and into southern Russia.

ON THE TERRACES

THE PARTNERSHIP THAT AROSE between people and grasses in the Middle East was not unique. Similar relationships with plants have evolved independently in many parts of the globe. One of the most significant featured another type of grass. It began in the Far East.

Six thousand years ago, around the estuaries and flood plains of southern China and Thailand, a tropical variety of grass was poised to become one of the most successful plants on earth. It demanded waterlogged conditions for most of its life and, if it were to be cultivated successfully, complex terracing

Opposite: The landscape of Bali has been transformed
to provide waterlogged conditions for growing rice.
Overleaf: The little egret is one of a few specialists that has
prospered from the spread of rice cultivation.

and irrigation methods were needed to simulate its natural requirements. Once societies developed sufficiently to provide this level of organisation, the success of rice was ensured. Rice growing soon spread and, even today, in much of the Far East human life still revolves around its cultivation.

A bird called the little egret takes off from the heronry at Petulu, on the Indonesian island of Bali. It is flying over scenery transformed for the promotion of this single crop, rice. Most of the rainforest disappeared several thousand years ago and the egret views a landscape that has been sculpted by human hands. Even the steepest hillsides and ravines are crafted into terraces that cling tenaciously to every indentation of the land.

Below the bird tiny Brueghelesque figures labour at sowing and trans-planting, harvesting and threshing. Because the rice requires such exacting conditions their lives are totally controlled by the crop. Rice shapes the structure of their society and the form of their religion.

The egret is one of a few select species that was able to profit from the alliance these people forged with rice. As the bird lands by the side of a flooded paddy field it looks for animals that have similarly thrived. When people cleared the rainforest and created irrigation canals they converted even the driest hillsides into extensive areas of marshland. This attracted marsh-loving animals such as frogs and eels and it is these creatures that the egret hunts. Such opportunists exist not on the rice itself but on the conditions created to ensure its survival.

As the crop develops it attracts raiders intent on devouring the rice before it is harvested. Tight flocks of mannikin finches descend on the ripening fields. As with wheat, the seed head of the rice no longer shatters when mature, so the finches strip the seeds directly from the stem. Considerable human effort is required to scare away these competitors. The birds soon become habituated to the sight of scarecrows and the sound of bamboo clappers and so at prime harvest time people have to spend entire days protecting the crop. Raiding mammals are less easily seen but they cause an equal degree of devastation.

THE RAT PACK

IN CHINA TODAY, WILD varieties of rice still grow around the mouth of the Yangtze river. Scurrying through these natural paddy fields and feeding from the fallen rice grains are black rats. Their ancestors were quick to benefit from the human promotion of these rats' natural food and soon spread into cultivated rice fields across the Far East.

The rats' lives are so in tune with that of the rice that they rely on hormones in the plants to control their breeding. This enables them to time

The black rat originally inhabited wild stands of rice in the
Far East. Once it encountered stored produce, however,
populations soon reached plague proportions.

their litters to coincide with peaks in the harvest.

Although the black rat's existence is entwined with the rice, it is a highly adaptable animal and, as soon as it sampled other forms of human food, it moved in to take advantage. As international trade increased the rats spread westwards through India and on to the Red Sea area of the Middle East. By the time of the Ancient Greek civilisation they had reached the Mediterranean and they were probably introduced into southern Europe by the Romans. In the early Middle Ages they were common throughout Europe.

For centuries black rats were the most successful mammal invaders of human foodstores. The house mouse was their only competitor and, where the two species occurred together, the black rat would oust the smaller mouse. Actual fights would be rare as odour signals left by the rats would be enough to discourage the mice. Unlike mice, however, the black rats could transmit diseases to humans. The most serious of these was bubonic plague, which, passed on to people via rat fleas, was responsible for the Black Death.

But the supremacy of the black rat could not last for ever. In eastern Central Asia, probably originally living along the banks of streams, another variety of rat eventually encountered human agriculture. Once this creature, the brown rat, had tasted the benefits of living alongside people, it became even more successful than the black rat. As well as being larger and more aggressive, it was also more adaptable, so wherever the two coincided the newcomer displaced the established black rat.

The brown rat came to share our lives at a relatively late date, not reaching Europe until the early eighteenth century. It was recorded in England in 1728, France in 1750, Norway in 1762 and by 1775 it had invaded North America. Contributing to its success was its prodigious reproductive rate. In one year, a pair of brown rats and their offspring can, theoretically, give rise to a thousand individuals and by the end of a second year the combined progeny of all these rats will approach half a million.

When the brown rat appeared, the black rat, a far better climber, became restricted to the tops of buildings or its former strongholds on ships and in ports. Only in the tropics did it manage to outnumber the brown rat.

The expansion in world exploration and trade that caused the brown rat to spread also allowed the human cultures based on wheat and rice to encounter the agricultural societies that had developed in Central and South America. These civilisations had evolved quite independently, based on alliances forged with completely different varieties of plants.

MEXICAN JUMPING BEANS

THE AGRICULTURAL TRADITION OF the New World is just as ancient as those of the Middle and Far East. Many plants with American origins were adopted by European colonists and are now familiar vegetables.

Around 9000 years ago, in the mountains of Mexico, squash and pumpkin began to be cultivated and, 2000 years later, several varieties of beans also joined a partnership with people. The association was later to provide the agricultural basis for the Aztec and Mayan civilisations.

In their wild state the form of the beans assisted the early farmers in their domestication. The original beans, which still grow in Mexico, have pods that, by violently twisting apart, propel their ripe seeds into the air This. explosive device is effective at dispersing the seeds but means that the pods are difficult to harvest. Fortunately, the beans occasionally displayed nonexplosive forms which the farmers found easier to gather.

Over many generations, the planting and gathering of these less volatile varieties created a race of beans that kept their seeds firmly in the pod when ripe. These beans now relied totally on people for their propagation, but they also profited from the care that was bestowed upon them. Their distant descendants can today be found growing in many suburban gardens in the guise of runner and French beans.

CORN ON THE COB

AT THE SAME TIME, yet another type of grass was beginning to attract the early Mexican farmers. It too was to become totally dependent on people for its survival. Today, its seeds are tightly packed in parcels that are handy for human gathering but useless for natural dispersal.

The plant is maize and its cob, with its convenience wrapping, must have developed many thousands of years ago. The original cobs were no longer than an inch in length and, unlike modern maize, their protective husks opened to shed the seeds when ripe.

The ancestor of maize is now extinct but a wild descendant, known as teosinte, can still be found in a few places in Mexico. In contrast, those varieties of maize that gave up their independent existence and opted for domestication ultimately joined wheat and rice as one of the three main crops of the world.

CHILLI ADDICTS

CROPS FURTHER SOUTH DEVELOPED separately from those grown in Mexico. One plant originally relied on chemical addiction to draw animals to it. Today we are attracted to exotic cuisines spiced with its pods and seeds.

As a macaw flies over the South American rainforest it searches for its favourite food. These fruits can be found growing wild in the forest but the jungle gardens of the Indians provide a richer selection of enticing varieties. The fruits are chillies and the reason they are popular with both birds and human cultivators is that they contain chemicals believed to cause a mild form of addiction. These substances are thought to release natural opiates in the brain and create a craving that draws animals to the plant.

The chilli seeds are naturally dispersed by birds like macaws, but once people had become addicted to their pungent taste the success of the domesticated plant was ensured. The chilli soon gained popularity around the world. When it reached Asia it became an essential cookery ingredient.

The gardens of South American Indians contain many other plants that are familiar to us. However, in their wild state some of these contain toxic, rather than pleasurable, chemicals and so must be eaten with care.

After eating a poisonous plant, red-and-green and scarlet macaws will go to a river bank to ingest clay. The clay acts as an antidote by neutralising the effects of the poison.

WHAT'S YOUR POISON?

MANY PLANTS CONTAIN POISONS, which can either kill the animals that eat them or cause dangerous side effects such as vomiting or abortion. Grazing mammals try to avoid these hazards by feeding selectively. They usually consume only small quantities of anything unfamiliar, while some secrete enzymes to neutralise toxins or even create new ones.

Toxic plants generally have a bitter taste which acts as a warning to any animal attempting to eat them. When macaws have fed on a poisonous plant they then fly across the forest canopy in search of an antidote. Hundreds of these multicoloured parrots descend on exposed river banks where they neutralise the effects of the chemicals by ingesting clay. The local Indians also imbibe clay to neutralise the toxins of many of the plants they eat. We treat stomach upsets in a similar way by taking kaolin.

Among the most lethal of the South American Indians' plants are the tubers we know as potatoes. In their original form these contain dangerous alkaloids and so before they could become the popular and inoffensive vegetables we know today they had to undergo considerable modification.

THE SPUD WE LIKE

THE DOMESTICATION OF THE potato began 4500 years ago, on the high slopes of the Andes, where melt water from the snowcaps created verdant valleys. The partnership between early mountain farmers and their plants ultimately gave rise to the Inca civilisation.

The first steps involved the help of a type of New World camel. In the area around Lake Titicaca, the wild ancestor of the llama, known as the guanaco, had begun to be domesticated. Part of its control involved the use of corrals for herding. Plant seeds, including those of the original potatoes, were passed out with the guanaco's dung and the animals' hooves acted as natural ploughs. The potatoes grew well in the newly fertilised soil and old deserted corrals became accidental gardens. Soon people deliberately cultivated the crops that grew there, using dung as manure.

The prototype potatoes required careful treatment to remove their toxins. But gradually, as the Indians selected the largest, most palatable tubers, they began to create a vegetable that had lost most of its poisonous alkaloids. Transformed in this way, the potato was to become the most successful vegetable in the world.

Once discovered and exported by the early explorers, the detoxified potatoes not only fed an increasing number of human mouths but they also attracted a delighted army of insect gourmets. To these new pests the cultivated potatoes proved particularly appetising. Not only had they lost the poisons that once defended the tuber but in the process they also abandoned an ingenious insect trap that had protected their leaves.

The leaves of wild potatoes are guarded by special hairs that act as a formidable barrier to alighting insects. If a leaf beetle tries to walk over the surface the hairs exude a sticky glue. As the beetle struggles to free itself it knocks into other hairs. On the end of each of these is a capsule that bursts open to release a chemical hardening agent – the same principle is used in commercial epoxy resins. Bonded to the leaf, the beetle dies and, as it decays, nitrogen is absorbed into the plant. Although this ingenious insect trap was vital to the vegetable's defences, by the time the potato had begun to colonise the world it had disappeared, along with the chemical weapon in the tubers.

When these newly vulnerable plants arrived in Colorado, in the United States, at the beginning of the nineteenth century, their smell attracted a local species of beetle that fed on buffalo burr, a plant related to the potato. This insect found the defenceless potato irresistible and, within two years, the Colorado beetle, with its familiar striped wing-cases, had invaded potato crops as far as the East Coast. It was soon to travel the globe.

From the same region of the Andes that gave birth to the potato came other crops, such as tomatoes, peanuts and lima beans. Around the world many other plants had embarked on an association with humans. As they were drawn into domestication they too began to change.

Agriculture, a process that began so gradually and on so many different fronts, was now gathering momentum and feeding increasingly large populations of people and animals. As the tradition of cultivation was passed down the human generations, the farmers began to make a more conscious effort to transform their plants. Of all these metamorphoses, perhaps the most remarkable were those that culminated in the cabbage.

CABBAGE CONVERSION

THE FIRST FORMS OF cabbage were leafy kales that grew wild around the Mediterranean. Like the early potatoes, these had a bitter taste which was due to the alkaloids present in their leaves. These chemicals were used to ward off attacks by insects but in one case they proved ineffective – against the caterpillars of the cabbage white butterfly. Far from being harmed, these insects could extract the poisons and actually incorporate them into their bodies as a chemical defence against attacks from birds.

Before the plant could become a useful component of the human diet the toxins had to be removed. People inevitably selected the larger and

The early domestication of the llamas in Peru also resulted in the domestication of the potato. Crops developed naturally in the deserted llama corrals.

more succulent plants for breeding and, as these tended to have lower concentrations of poisons, so the toxicity of the vegetables began to decrease. Besides removing the alkaloids, different groups of farmers also improved various of the plants' physical aspects. These enhanced varieties became so dissimilar that they were eventually regarded as separate vegetables.

The farmers of Roman times expanded the stem to tuber-like proportions to create kohlrabi. Later, in Germany, the terminal bud enlarged to become the superbud known as a cabbage. In Belgium farmers augmented the side buds to create the Brussels sprout and, in Cyprus, improvement of the stem and flowers gave rise to broccoli. By the Middle Ages the crowning glory of these transformations had appeared, a single flower head enhanced to spectacular dimensions – the cauliflower.

Even though the cabbage now appeared in many different guises, it still attracted the cabbage white butterfly. The egg-laying adult butterfly relies on the smell of alkaloids to locate the plant and concentrations of these toxins had certainly been reduced, but they had not been removed entirely. This is just as well as without a seasoning of these noxious chemicals cabbage would appear equally tasteless to humans.

The changing shapes of the plants did not confuse the butterflies, as they ultimately recognise these vegetables by their rough silhouettes standing out against a dark, contrasting background. The fact that plants were now grown spaced out in rows cleared of distracting weeds actually made it easier for the butterflies to identify them. The butterflies' visual system only became confused when farmers developed a red cabbage, as their eyes are tuned to the colour green so these plants proved harder to find.

GALLOPING GOURMETS

JUST AS THE NEW, highly modified plant varieties attracted their own consumers so did the foodstores filled by the expanding and changing harvest. Across the world, 15 per cent of all stored produce is still eaten by animals other than humans. No matter how obscure or altered, each product attracts its own insect connoisseur and their favoured speciality is reflected in what the creatures came to be called.

Dried fruit attracts the prune mite, while coffee and cocoa beans become infested by the coffee weevil. Dried animal products such as hide and skin are food for the bacon beetle, which also infests larders of bacon and ham.

Cheeses prove irresistible to cheese mites, but their gourmet lives are often terminated when they are consumed by humans along with the cheese. The cheese skipper rarely suffers this fate, however, as this fly maggot makes itself conspicuous by its bizarre method of getting around. It progresses via a succession of leaps, executed by grasping its end with its mouth and springing into the air as it lets go.

The warehouse moth has the most unspecific tastes of all and will voraciously consume cocoa beans, almonds, dried fruit and many other stored foods. Undeterred by the dangers of nicotine it has become the world's major tobacco pest.

Perhaps the most specialised consumers are those that have acquired a taste for alcoholic beverages. The larvae of the wine moth bores holes in wine corks and feeds on the mould that grows there. But the most remarkable of all is a tiny nematode worm that has taken to drink in the bierkellers of Austria and Germany. It tunnels into beer mats and gains its refreshment from bacteria multiplying on the beer splashed by revellers.

Such weird specialists were accidental beneficiaries of the spread of

In Papua New Guinea deforestation for agriculture began 9000 years ago. Today, it continues at an accelerating rate across the world.

cultivation. However, the changes that agriculture wrought affected more than just the animals that could thrive off the crop and its produce. As the domesticated plants spread they displaced the original vegetation as well as the creatures that formerly sheltered there.

THE VANISHING FOREST

IN SOUTH AMERICA AND Papua New Guinea farmers slash and burn patches of forest to clear the ground and release nutrients for their crops. These small clearings are then filled with a range of cultivated plants that parallel the forest's natural diversity. Once the crop has been harvested the forest is allowed to regenerate.

This type of swidden agriculture was also practised by the early farmers as they cleared forest to make way for new crops. But as human populations grew there was less attempt to allow the forest to return and, instead of growing mixed crops, a trend developed towards fields with single varieties. The process of deforestation and soil impoverishment was under way.

Nine thousand years ago trees were being cut down to make way for crops in India and New Guinea. The first clearing of the South and Central American rainforest for agriculture started 7000 years ago, and the same began to happen 3000 years ago in Africa.

The main effect of destroying areas of forest was to change the balance of the existing species. Some formerly common species became rare but certain scarce species found new opportunities. Starlings, originally confined to the steppes around the Caspian and Black Seas, were one of the birds to profit when agriculture first spread across Europe. Starlings specialise in probing the soil with an open bill. Their eyes can swivel to look for insect larvae in the bill but by a useful modification they can also turn their eyes backwards to look for predators approaching from behind. They were perfectly adapted to a life in short grassland and, when farmers extended the area of natural grasses by removing trees and replacing them with cereals, they were able to spread far from their original home.

Such opportunists were quick to exploit the new landscapes created when neolithic farmers reached Britain around 5000 years ago. Until then the land was largely covered by broad-leafed woodlands of oak and elm. These mature trees shaded the forest floor and restricted the growth of grasses and herbaceous plants. The farmers began by clearing the light wooded ridges but the deforestation soon intensified and by the iron age much of the original forest had become fragmented and replaced by fields. By then the balance of animal life had been transformed.

WINNERS AND LOSERS

ALTHOUGH THE CHANGES WERE drastic very few species actually became extinct as the pockets of woodland that remained acted as refuges. The main mammals to suffer were those like the bear and wolf that men hunted. Only five species of bird were lost to Britain, including those like the honey buzzard that required extensive forest cover.

For many birds the landscape was changed in their favour. The winners included those that nested in trees but needed open areas for foraging, such as common buzzards, carrion crows and magpies. Rooks, which feed almost exclusively on short grassland or ploughed fields, probably did not even exist in northern Europe until people opened up the forest. Birds that were formerly restricted to the forest edge also found a chance to expand their

Queleas are finches of the African savannah. Their vast numbers
can devastate the cereal crops that have replaced the natural
grasses for which they used to forage.

populations. Partridge, quail, skylarks and lapwings made their home in the
new farmlands. The wood pigeon even changed its breeding season to early
autumn in order to profit from the grain left after the harvest.

No matter where in the world agriculture travelled there were resident
opportunists ready to move on board. In Australia raucous flocks of parrots,
such as galahs and sulphur crested cockatoos, strip bare fields of sunflowers
before the seeds can be harvested. Flocks of these intelligent and perceptive
birds can number several thousand and they are adept at outwitting the
farmer's attempts at destroying them.

What the parrots achieve by guile the quelea finches of Africa achieve
by sheer force of numbers. Queleas are seed-feeding birds of the semi-arid
savannah. Their technique is to glean fallen seeds from the ground by
hopping in vast legions along the ground. Those that reach the back of the
flock fly to the front and their continual motion results in a rolling black
cloud spreading an all-consuming shadow across the countryside. When they
envelop cereal crops the destruction can appear awesome to farmers. But the

quelea are simply continuing their natural foraging behaviour and the confrontation only arises because alien grasses, succoured through irrigation, have been planted in their natural home.

Equally appreciative of introduced plants are army worms, striped caterpillars living in southern Africa. Each year, provisioned by the crops, battalions of army worms begin to form. They change into moths and then, under the cover of darkness, squadrons of the flying insects head north. They descend on farmers' fields to lay their eggs and create new hungry regiments to assault the crops. Alternating between being ground troops and an air force, and their numbers reinforcing at every encampment, they eventually achieve invincible strength. Legions of the army worms then lay waste whatever crop they find. Their incursions may take them as far as Ethiopia or even the Yemen.

Wherever crops introduced a new source of food there were creatures waiting in the wings to profit from the agricultural bonanza. But the changes to the landscape pushed out former residents and as the process intensified the losers began to outnumber the winners.

PROFITING FROM THE PRAIRIES

AS SNOW GEESE FLY SOUTH across the northern United States on their yearly migration they are crossing a country that has been transformed. The revolution began as soon as the first colonists reached North America and within 200 years they had removed more woodland than had disappeared in Europe in the previous 2000.

The migrating snow geese now look down on a landscape dominated by just a few species of plants. The central migration route that stretches from Hudson Bay to the Gulf of Mexico takes the snow geese across the prairies of North America. Flying at an average speed of 35 miles an hour it takes them four or five days to complete their journey.

At one time the landscape below them would have consisted of over a hundred prairie herbs and grasses grazed by vast herds of bison. They now see only the grasses of agriculture, mainly wheat and corn. These are two of the three main crops of the world and for several days of their flight the snow geese encounter little else. These plants are the descendants of species that allied themselves with people many thousands of years ago in the Middle East and Central America. As the geese fly further south they encounter the descendants of a grass once confined to marshes in the Far East. This rice is now the third main crop of the world.

All these varieties of grass are grown on such an intensive basis that few

Many species of geese, including barnacle geese, have prospered from the landscape changes created by agriculture.

competitors get a look in. Those that can flourish from the crop survive in spectacular numbers. The snow geese often complete their entire migration without feeding but they are joined by countless millions of grain-feeders which stop en route to snack on the crop. The most numerous of these are red-wing blackbirds.

These are birds of wetlands and marshes, but when their original homes were drained to make way for cereal crops, rather than undergo a decline, their numbers actually multiplied. They adapted to feeding from the crops and spread with them over much of the eastern and central United States as well as California and southern Canada. In late summer they fatten themselves on ripening corn, green oats and barley before accompanying snow geese on their migration south.

When they reach their winter roosts, the cacophony of their arrival noisily proclaims their success. A single roost may contain a phenomenal 20 million of these opportunists. They are joined in almost equal numbers by grackles, related birds whose populations also boomed spectacularly on the new monocultural prairies.

Nearby, their migration over, a blizzard of snow geese descends like snowflakes onto any area of open water. They roost here for protection but in the morning search out winter pasture on the farmers' fields. Their populations, like those of barnacle, greylag and many other European geese, have also undergone an explosion due to the changes wrought by agriculture.

These birds have profited as much as humans from the alliance that people forged with a few favoured plants. The invertebrates that are regarded as pests have fared even better. No matter how much human effort is put into exterminating them they still thrive along with crop.

DANGEROUS DEPENDENCY

WE HAVE MODIFIED OR TRANSFORMED the plants that we once simply gathered. In the process we have become dependent on fewer and fewer species. The four main crop plants of the world – wheat, rice, maize and potatoes – supply us with more food than the next 26 combined. We take up an increasing amount of the earth's land surface to grow the few we favour.

Previous page: Red-winged blackbirds are native to the wetlands of North America, but their numbers increased spectacularly when their homes were replaced by cereal crops.

These plants now rely on us for life but we are equally dependent on them for our own survival.

The original plants from which our crops were derived are now rare and some are even extinct. The highly modified forms we grow have few natural defences and so ultimately their partnership with us is a fragile one. It is easy for other organisms to hijack the partnership and gain control. Plagues of locusts, army worms and quelea can still create devastation in Africa while the Irish potato famine of the last century was caused by a fungus that found a way of exploiting a partnership we believed had been created for our benefit alone.

We so rely on these few species of plant that failure of one crop can cause starvation for millions. Many of the famines of the present day are due to large human populations depending on just a few highly modified species often poorly adapted to the local climate.

But, although delicate, the relationship with plants that we unwittingly entered all those years ago was responsible for the growth of human civilisation as well as the immense and ever-burgeoning human populations of today. If we had continued the way of life of the Bushmen the maximum sustainable human population of the world would have been 20 million instead of the five billion plus at which it currently stands.

This phenomenal increase has been at the expense of many forms of other life, many of which now face extinction. Even so, a large percentage of our crops are now grown deliberately for other animals. These creatures are so familiar that we hardly give them a thought but they started to associate with us when we began to grow crops and their numbers now far outstrip our own. They are the domesticated animals of our farms and homes.

CHAPTER

3

PARTNERS
FOR LIFE

I N THE GARDEN OF ALMOST every suburban home, herds of domesticated animals are reared and milked for food. This pastoral scene
usually goes unnoticed because the farmers are only a few millimetres
long and their flocks are grazed on the leaves of roses.

The miniature backyard ranchers are another type of ant – black ants –
and their livestock are the aphids that human gardeners know as greenfly.
As the aphids suck sap from our roses they save up a sugary by-product for
the ants. The ants milk the aphids for this sweet fluid by stroking them with
their antennae. In return for this secretion the ants defend the aphids from
predators such as ladybirds and lacewing larvae. Many ants and aphids have
this kind of partnership. If the herds of aphids grow too large the ants will
move them to new pastures. The ants that tend the bean aphid even overwinter their livestock in underground stalls, a form of transhumance also
practised by human herders and their cattle in the Swiss Alps.

As we saw previously, ants had beaten humans to the idea of agriculture
by several million years and they had also begun to farm animals around
the same time. In comparison, the domestication of animals by people is a
new practice, having started a mere 10 000 years ago. Even more recently,
human population pressures have changed animal-rearing practices in industrialised countries out of all recognition, transforming the close personal
relationship of people with their food animals into the unnatural production
line of the factory farm.

As was the case with the development of agriculture, humans did not
consciously initiate the original process of domestication – it happened as a
natural extension of existing relationships with wild creatures. All the animals
involved had a social structure that already predisposed them to a life

The donkey was domesticated in North Africa 6000 years ago
and by Egyptian times it was being used as a beast of burden.

entwined with human societies. This development was so inevitable that it occurred independently in many parts of the world. An impression of how the domestication of animals may have started can be gathered today in the remote highlands of Papua New Guinea.

A PIG IN A POKE

A BLACK KITE SOARS OVER the lush virgin rainforest of the Shreader Mountain range. Suddenly, as it lifts up over a ridge, a new landscape is revealed, the unbroken forest giving way to a hillside covered in grass. But this is no ordinary grass – it is tall enough to hide a man and it is on fire.

Through the smoke, the kite watches as human figures follow the leading edge of the flames. They are hunters. As the kite watches for dead insects and small mammals caught up in the inferno, the humans look for larger prey. They wait, armed with bows and arrows, for pigs to appear. When finally flushed from cover, the pigs encounter a barrage of arrows as they try to reach the shelter of the forest.

The hunters have only been known to the outside world since 1984, and are known as the Hagerhai. Their ancestors have, over the last 6000 years, created in Papua New Guinea a patchwork landscape of primary rainforest interspersed with fields of giant kunai grass. It is this grass that the Hagerhai periodically burn to encircle their prey.

Our hunting forefathers must have manipulated wild animal populations in a similar way. But how did domestication begin? The Hagerhai show that the first stages could have come about easily.

Sometimes the smoke on the hillside reaches a sow and piglets. Warned of the approaching inferno she guides her young to shelter, grunting to maintain contact with them. As the fire and the people close in, she breaks for cover. In the rush the piglets often become separated. Calling frantically, they career around searching for their mother. Even if she escapes, the piglets will never see her again, for within seconds human hands pluck them from the smouldering ground. Squealing with fright they are thrust into string bags and carried, wriggling, back to the village. The trauma over, they now rest in the more gentle hands of Hagerhai women, their new foster mothers.

Each woman will lavish on her piglet the same care and affection that she gives to her own children. She will even suckle the animal on her breasts. A deep bond develops between the piglet and its new parent, which continues until the pig matures. It is then allowed to return to the wild to breed. Although it now lives like a wild pig it will return to the woman whenever she calls.

An intense attachment develops between the pigs and the women, but the Hagerhai never forget the real reason for the relationship. Their diet is deficient in protein and without meat they would be susceptible to malnutrition and disease. When meat is needed, often for a ceremonial feast, a pig is killed. Its ultimate fate is an inescapable matter of human survival, but even so the women who rear the animals still mourn the pig's death. Significantly, the men, who remain detached from the rearing of the pigs, are the ones who perform the killing. The women eat the meat, but they are never sure which pig it came from.

Because the Hagerhai are primarily hunter-gatherers they show only the earliest stages of rearing animals. The relationship is limited to controlling wild pig populations and rearing wild-caught young. The pigs are not bred in captivity and have to return to the wild to breed. When the entire human race existed by hunting it would have been common for the young of hunted animals to be brought home and reared in this way.

Only when people settled to grow crops would it have been possible for more permanent relationships to develop. Even so, one animal did manage to forge a lasting partnership with early humans and it still shares the lives of the Hagerhai today. It not only lives and breeds alongside them, but braves the smoke and fire to join in the hunt. It is the dog.

HUNTING PACT

ALL DOGS WERE ORIGINALLY descended from wolves. The classic partnership, between a man and his dog, that ultimately proved so successful, was only possible because humans and wolves shared similarities in their social and hunting behaviour. These resemblances can still be seen as the Hagerhai and their dogs hunt together.

Before wolves set off to look for prey they come together and reinforce their feeling of allegiance by howling. Similarly, the Hagerhai chant communally before the start of a hunt and their dogs accompany them, emitting an eerie singing sound. When hunting, wolves communicate using a complex set of body signals, including facial expressions. The Hagerhai also use visual signs and facial expressions to make themselves understood through the roar of the fire. Their dogs react to these visual cues too, just as they do to those of other dogs.

As wolves near their quarry they will work together in finding and chasing their prey. The Hagerhai do the same and the dogs help by sniffing out the hunted pig through the smokescreen created by the smouldering grass. When the pig breaks for cover the dogs race ahead of the men and use the techniques of the wolf pack to corner and hold the pig at bay until the men arrive.

Above: The Hagerhai of Papua New Guinea burn kunai grass to flush out wild pigs. Top right: Dogs are important hunting companions and afterwards share in the spoils. Below right: Captured piglets are taken home and reared by the Hagerhai women as though they were their own children.

The wolf pack is held together by a hierarchy of dominant and submissive individuals. Although, compared with many human societies, Hagerhai clans are only loosely structured, their dogs continue to have ranks among themselves and they all act submissively to humans. Although the dogs and the Hagerhai huddle together as the pigs sizzle over the campfires, when the meat is distributed the people eat first and the dogs have to content themselves with any scraps left over. Similarly, dominant wolves always finish eating before others dare approach.

As human hunters and wolves shared so many aspects of behaviour, it was inevitable that a more permanent relationship would develop between them. The partnership began before the advent of agriculture. Dogs were hunting with people 12 000 years ago, in the area that is now Iraq, but wolves appear to have been domesticated wherever they lived alongside people and this alliance probably has an even more ancient history.

The association began when hunters brought home orphaned wolf cubs, just as, today, the Hagerhai foster piglets. The bonding between the young animal and the human that reared it was due to a process known as imprinting.

BIRD BOND

IN ANOTHER PART OF THE highlands of Papua New Guinea, Huli Wigmen and other tribes hunt the ostrich-like cassowary. If a hen bird is killed her young will often be taken alive. The orphaned chick perceives the strange creature that towers above it as its mother and immediately begins to follow him. The imprinting is so strong that, if the chick becomes separated for even a moment, it calls incessantly, using a soft whistling contact sound, until the man returns. It even shelters under its foster parent's legs as it would with a bird. The bonding appears to work both ways and the Huli Wigman responds with the kind of parental care and affection expected of him.

The cassowary chick is a demanding infant. Each day the man needs to find vast quantities of food to supply the chick's insatiable appetite. His fostering has to continue for the year it takes for the chick to reach maturity. Over this period the only reward for his devotion is the prestige gained in owning a cassowary chick and the company the bird gives.

As the cassowary matures, other humans are regarded as sexual rivals and, as the bird may attempt to disembowel them with well-aimed kicks to

*Opposite: A captured cassowary chick will follow its
human foster parent, a Huli Wigman, wherever he goes.
Overleaf: In Bali, a duck shepherd guides his flock
to the paddy fields where they will scavenge on fallen grain.*

the stomach, it has to be penned. The relationship the cassowary had with its foster parent then inevitably begins to break down. This distancing is fortunate for eventually the man will have to kill the bird at a special ceremony. After its death, all parts of the bird are put to ceremonial use: these include feathers to decorate the Wigmen's elaborate head-dresses and bones to make daggers.

In Bali imprinting is used to control ducks. At hatching the duckling's 360-degree vision attempts to make sense of the confusing patterns of light shade that it sees. It is programmed to follow any large moving object. In the natural world this would invariably be its mother, but here it is frequently a human being and the duckling readily waddles after this person instead. The ducklings also imprint socially on each other and consequently always huddle together.

From an early age they are always fed next to a stick decorated with a white flag and this also becomes an important security symbol to them. Because of this imprinting, when the duck shepherd leads his quacking flock to the paddy fields to forage, they stay together and can easily be controlled by movements of the stick.

The significant difference between these ducks and the cassowary chick is that, having been brought up together, they recognise each other as potential sexual partners when they reach maturity.

Although mammals show more flexibility in their natural behaviour, wolf cubs would have also imprinted on their human rearers. If they were to breed successfully they would have to be reared with other wolves. Once this happened the process of domestication could begin.

DESIGNER ANIMALS

CHANGES TO THE BASIC wolf type appeared quickly, arising spontaneously through the exercise of human preferences. Wolf cubs that had a docile nature would tend to be favoured by their human foster parents and, if they survived to breed, this characteristic would be passed on to their offspring. Individuals with qualities that set them apart from their wild relatives would also be favoured.

Unusual shapes and distinctive markings, a disadvantage in the wild, appealed to the wolves' human partners and consequently animals with these features and their progeny began to thrive. The early dogs developed into two main types; in one variety the face became shortened and the skull developed a pronounced forehead, as seen in the mastiff, while the other took on the elongated head shape now found in the greyhound.

The early stages of domestication involved little deliberate selection for these features, but once people, rather than other predators, influenced which animals survived, extreme changes from the wild type became inevitable.

Most domesticated animals underwent similar changes. Dominant or aggressive animals were now at a disadvantage and so docile and easily manageable creatures started to do well. As small animals were more controllable, so the body reduced in size as well. Over time the brain became proportionally smaller, the jaw became shortened and a layer of fat developed beneath the skin. Many of these changes were due to the animals retaining juvenile characteristics into adulthood. Animals with distinct markings or features, such as lop-ears or curled tail, were particularly favoured.

Creatures that were kept for food began to show high fertility, rapid growth and, in particular, they became efficient at converting plants into animal protein. The first of the food animals to be domesticated were sheep and goats.

THE SHEEP AND THE GOATS

TEN THOUSAND YEARS AGO, on the hills surrounding the Fertile Crescent, in the area that is now Iraq, herds of wild sheep known as mouflon, as well as wild goats, found their environment was changing. The tree cover was disappearing and being replaced by stands of succulent grasses and other plants. The mouflon and goats found the enticing greenery irresistible but grazing them proved difficult. The plants were protected by people.

Although many of the crop-raiders were killed by these farmers, the herds were still inexorably drawn to such tempting pastures. The agriculturalists began to recognise the value of having meat animals so close to hand and, although they still protected their best crops they also encouraged the herds to stay by providing water and protection. Over time the sheep and goat populations closest to the villages began to consist of individuals with the tamest nature.

The social structure of these herds shared an important similarity with that of their human neighbours. Both societies were controlled by a single dominant leader. A human herdsman was able to take over the role of the dominant sheep and the animals became accustomed to being herded by this familiar person.

Through this relationship the sheep gained protection from predators and a ready supply of food. Although slaughtered for meat, their populations fared better than those in the wild. As their numbers increased, through human protection, they began to spread away from their natural home. They travelled with the early farmers as they moved westwards into Europe and north and east into Asia. Seven thousand years ago they had reached Syria,

Goats were domesticated along with sheep 10 000 years ago in the Middle East. Today, their natures are perfectly adapted for a life protected by people.

Greece and Crete, and within another 1000 years they had arrived in Scandinavia and Britain. Goats showed a similar expansion in their range.

As sheep herding spread, various methods of controlling the flock developed. Humans usually took on the role of flock leader but in parts of Europe a sheep was nominated to act as the shepherd's agent. In Italy they still carry out this role today. A castrated ram or ewe is reared apart from the herd and trained to respond to simple commands. Released back into the flock it becomes the herd leader and controls the flock's movements by reacting to the shepherd's instructions.

ONE MAN AND HIS DOG

DOGS WERE ALSO USED to control the early herds but they were hampered by the sheep's natural defensive behaviour. On the Orkney island of North Ronaldsay sheep retain the original defence of scattering when attacked by a predator. They have to be controlled by a special kind of sheepdog, one that hunts instead of herds. The dog waits until the shepherd singles out a sheep and then gives chase. In a flying leap it grabs the sheep's throat and grapples it to the ground. Trained to suppress its natural desire to kill, the dog simply holds the animal, unharmed, until the shepherd arrives.

Once sheep, through selective breeding, lost this tendency to scatter, as still seen in Orkney, they became far easier to control. Sheep that, when chased, clustered together as a flock could easily be herded by dogs or people. To herd such sheep, modern sheepdogs rely on the same methods that a wolf pack uses to surround its prey. Instead of taking its cue from the movements of the rest of the pack, the dog is trained to respond to the commands of the shepherd. An essential part of its training involves suppressing the natural desire to close in for the bite.

Sheepdogs have always had a secondary role, guarding flocks against attack from predators. In Italy dogs have been specially developed for the purpose. These marrema dogs actually live inside the flocks. Deliberately made particularly docile, they are accepted by the sheep as part of the herd. They even look like sheep. This wolf in sheep's clothing has been created by selective breeding. Ironically, it now defends the flock against attack from wild wolves.

This creation of the ultimate sheepdog shows how far the controlled breeding of an animal can transform its appearance away from the wild form. In sheep, one of the main changes brought about by domestication was the loss of the stiff outer coat and the growth of a woolly fleece undercoat which was retained all year. Goats also changed their appearance. The earliest goats had scimitar horns but later a variety with twisted horns appeared and was preferred by human herdsmen. Both species became more docile as a result of domestication.

TAKING THE BULL BY THE HORNS

THE CONTROL OF CATTLE must have been very risky for the humans involved until compliant breeds had been created. Like sheep, cattle were also attracted to the crops of the early farmers and the process of taming would have been similar. Human domination would have been made easier by the use of a mineral irresistible to the cattle.

Salt is vital to most animals and in mineral-deficient areas they will travel great distances to find it. In the Assam hills of India the mithan, a local variety of cattle descended from the formidable wild gaur, obtains this essential mineral from people. The mithan roams the forest during the day but in the evening it seeks the protection of the village where it receives a gift of salt. So strong is their craving for salt that herds, left to roam deep in the forest for weeks or even months, will come to humans as soon as they hear their calls. Simply by providing salt licks the tribesmen maintain the upper hand.

The mithan is kept as a symbol of wealth and status and animals are only killed for religious sacrifice. It appears that the first cattle had this kind of spiritually oriented relationship with people and certainly bulls were an object of worship. This reverence for cattle, and particularly bulls, was a feature of many early civilisations and persists today in Indian culture.

The first cattle to associate with humans were aurochs. These animals are now extinct but their domesticated descendants can be found throughout the world. Later other local species of cattle became domesticated, separately. In Asia, in the Indus valley, the water buffalo began life in human company. In Indonesia descendants of the native betang became the dainty and doe-eyed variety of cattle found in Bali, Java and Borneo. In the mountains of Tibet the long-haired yak proved to be the perfect partner for high-altitude existence. It too was controlled by providing salt licks.

CHERISHED CATTLE

ALTHOUGH THE RELATIONSHIP BETWEEN the aurochs' descendants and people have undergone many changes, a close partnership continues today among the pastoralists of East Africa.

In southern Sudan, smoky plumes of dust regularly waft across the parched scrubland. They come from the hooves of cattle on their way to find fresh pasture. Like all cattle they are guided by a herd leader, but rather than a dominant bull, they are escorted by a member of the Dinka tribe.

These people are attentive herd leaders. As they walk they inspect the cows, removing any irritating ticks and regularly petting them. Each man knows the personality of every cow and is sensitive to their individual requirements. In the dry season the men suffer the blistering mid-day sun and, in the rainy season, the onslaught of mosquitoes, in order to stay with their charges. Each day they walk many kilometres to ensure that their cattle reach the best pasture. After feeding the animals are led to water and in the evening they are taken back to the village. The cattle gain so much from the

*The water buffalo was first domesticated in the Indus
valley. It still needs to be given daily access to water
in order to thrive.*

relationship that the Dinka believe that it was the cows that initiated the
process of domestication.

Back in the village, where the cattle are corralled for the night, even
more privileged animals await the men's return. In adolescence, every man
is given a finely patterned castrated steer to cherish. All Dinka cattle have
spectacular horns but this animal has the finest of all. The horns are bound
as they grow, to create an impressive decoration.

This steer receives the most lavish attention of all. It is spared the daily
trek to fresh pasture and instead is fed in the village. When the man returns
he sings to it. Calmed by the sounds of his human companion the steer listens

impassively to the songs he cannot understand. These compositions are performed in his praise. At night the man will sleep with his steer.

Besides the cherished song-oxen, each family looks after a herd of around 50 cattle. The cattle represent wealth and are usually only exchanged as part of a dowry payment. Every product of the cow is utilised: her milk is drunk or made into butter, her urine is used for tanning hides or for dying hair, her dung is burnt as fuel and her ash is used as toothpaste or skin decoration.

The cows react to this human devotion by being placid and compliant. Sometimes a man approaches a cow armed with a bow and arrow. Such is her trust she hardly struggles as the bow is fired at point blank range. Blood pours from the wound and is caught in a hide container – later it will be drunk. This blood-letting is as painless as donating blood and the wound heals rapidly. On special occasions a cow might be killed for meat but she is treated as a respected participant in a religious sacrifice.

This close, symbiotic relationship between people and cattle is also found among the Nuer in Sudan and further south into Kenya among the Samburu and the Masai. The bond that has developed ensures the survival of the tribespeople in otherwise inhospitable regions. The cattle have also gained from the partnership. They are protected from predators, whereas their wild ancestor, the aurochs, is now extinct.

The Masai live with their cattle in areas rich in wild game and the herds frequently encounter their natural enemies. The cattle's eyes are designed to scan for predators: the centre of their retina is delineated into a strip of high resolution which brings the horizon into sharp relief. But these cattle rarely bother to look and instead they rely on their human herders. During the day lions flee at the sight or smell of the Masai and at night the thorn fence that encircles the village creates an impregnable fortress. For these cattle their human guardians are both protector and predator.

HUMAN PREDATOR

IT IS THE ULTIMATE TRUTH that all life ends in death. All animals – humans are a recent and notable exception – end their lives as food for others. This is necessary and unavoidable. The whole complex web of life depends on this recycling. Only a small percentage of animals ever reach maturity and their populations are held in balance through continual cropping by predators.

Cattle have allowed the Masai to survive in otherwise inhospitable areas. Their human companions act as both protector and predator.

Domestication continues the process. In this case humans do the killing but, unlike other predators, they also provision their prey and guard them from wild predators. Through this protection and control, domesticated animals have also become more numerous. Often their counterparts living naturally have shown a corresponding decline.

The wild ancestor of the cow is now extinct, the wild mouflon is rare and even the wolf has been exterminated over much of its range. In contrast, their domesticated descendants are some of the most numerous creatures on earth. These animals have achieved numerical success but for some it has been at a cost.

PARTNERSHIP OR EXPLOITATION?

WHEN ANIMALS FIRST ENTERED a partnership with people there was a degree of equality in the relationship. They gained a reliable source of food as well as protection. These early relationships were characterised by the type of respect shown by the Dinka, which at times became a religious reverence. As their breeding came under increasing human influence, the animals were transformed from their original wild forms. Selected for docility over the centuries, they became increasingly manageable. Eventually they had become so physically modified that their lives were totally under people's control. What happened then depended on the nature of human societies they had entered.

The water buffalo races that take place near Negara town in Bali present a stark contrast to the attitude the Dinka have to their cattle. The races arose when farmers began competing with their neighbours in bringing the harvest home or ploughing a field. Eventually the contests became formalised into a yearly event and the ploughs or carts were replaced by two-wheeled chariots.

Two pairs at a time race around a circuitous 4-kilometre route and the animals are whipped into a thunderous charge by the charioteer. Although nothing separates the animals from the spectators, such is the acceptance of their subservient role that the buffaloes rarely breach the human wall. Such control is possible with a highly domesticated animal. It typifies the relationship that many agriculturalists developed with their charges.

Through domestication farmers were able to exist away from wild animals. The docile and compliant creatures they could now dominate helped reinforce a feeling of mental separation from the natural world. Humans

Previous pages: Buffalo racing in Bali. Domestication can quickly lead to domination.

began to believe in their own superiority. Although people depended more than ever on their livestock for food or for muscle power, they were in a position to exploit them, particularly those animals that laboured in the fields.

BEASTS OF BURDEN

NO IMAGE SO SYMBOLISES A dominated animal than a fully laden donkey. These animals were brought under human control 6000 years ago in the desert regions of North Africa, where the few remaining wild asses are fighting extinction today. By Egyptian times they were being used as beasts of burden, to help tread seeds into the soil and for threshing.

From North Africa they eventually spread into Europe, but as desert animals they were ill-equipped to deal with life in cooler climes and they rarely thrived in the far north. They are still used almost exclusively for hard labour. The horse, their close relative, has fared better.

Although the horse had been extensively hunted since palaeolithic times it was the last of the main animals to be domesticated and by then people had gained experience with many other species. The partnership began 5500 years ago in the area of the southern Ukraine. From the beginning the relationship was special and horses were regarded as symbols of prestige. As they are slow to mature they were less valuable as meat producers but soon proved their worth as draught animals. Horses could transport goods far more quickly than people and twice as fast as oxen.

The nature of their society predisposed horses to a more equal partnership with people. Although they have dominance hierarchies, so a human could assume the role of a lead horse, bonds of friendship frequently develop between individual horses and the same attachments can be transferred to people. Horses demonstrate this friendship to each other by mutual grooming. Humans provide similar signals whenever they groom a horse.

HORSE TRADE

ALTHOUGH A CLOSE RELATIONSHIP was necessary for people to handle and keep together a herd of horses, it took 1500 years for the idea of riding to catch on. Horses have a natural aversion to what they perceive as a predator on their back and will buck until they dislodge the attacker. The first people to overcome this reaction lived in Mesopotamia but horse-riding soon became widespread across Europe. Controlling a horse requires a deep bond between person and rider. Among the nomadic pastoralists of what is now Hungary and the Ukraine, the relationship resembled that of the Dinka and their cattle. The synthesis of rider and horse allowed them to work together and they became formidable conquerors of neighbouring tribes.

Horses were now used more for warfare than transport. The structure of their society, based on a loose hierarchy and, perhaps more importantly, friendship bonds, made them ideal for this role. In horse society a high-ranking mare leads, followed by the rest of the group in order of status, the foals following the mares in ascending order of age and the stallion bringing up the rear. In a cavalry charge or convoy the human rider assumes the role of lead mare or stallion and holds the group together.

In Western Europe, a group of much smaller Celtic horses developed and were held in similar high esteem by their owners. As horses were traded or captured in warfare two main groups eventually evolved. The differences can still be seen in the fine-boned, 'hot-blooded' Arabian breeds now valued for racing and the stockier, 'cold-blooded' northern horses, which tend to be used as draught animals. The original wild horses had a stiff erect mane, but a mutation soon created the familiar flowing version.

If the horse had not entered a partnership with humans it would now be extinct. Like many species, it traded its independence for survival. The tarpan was exterminated at the turn of the century and the only other existing wild horse, Przewalski's, no longer lives in the natural state. Through its alliance with humans the horse avoided extinction and has even been able to repopulate areas it once inhabited at the end of the last ice age.

The close relationship essential in keeping and controlling a horse has ensured that it has never been exploited in the same way as many other domesticated animals. In the desert regions of the world similar relationships developed with the camel.

DESERT ALLIANCE

IN THE TENERE DESERT OF Niger, as the wind whips the tips of mountainous dunes, sand peels off newly scalloped peaks then spirals across the land. As the storm increases in ferocity, the air soon becomes a roaring mass of dust and grit that races in a choking cloud.

Few living creatures can survive this abrasive deluge, but camels are routinely exposed to the brutal sandblasting with few ill-effects. Their muscular nostrils close to keep out the onslaught of suffocating grains and their

Opposite above: Dartmoor ponies exhibit the stocky and heavy-boned characteristics of northern breeds.
Opposite below: A Bedouin will look after his camel with great care. Their close relationship is vital for survival.

eyes wash away the penetrating sand with a cleansing flood of tears. Long, brush-like eyelashes also act as sand filters, and as they peer through them they can gain an impression of their human associates, nestling for shelter in the protective nook formed by their bodies.

When the sandstorm subsides the people appear. These are the Tuareg, blue-shrouded herdsmen who still maintain the traditional nomadic way of life. They rely on the camels in order to survive in this forbidding landscape and they are only too aware of the value of their animals. Camels not only come through the desert storms but also tolerate suffocating heat and drought. They can lose 40 per cent of their body water comfortably and, when food is unobtainable, utilise fat stored in the hump. The Tuareg, like other desert nomads, such as the Bedouin, depend on the camels to transport goods across this inhospitable terrain.

They treat their camels as valued companions, removing annoying ticks from their skin and feeding them succulent titbits by hand whenever they are available. The Tuareg make use of the herd's natural structure to maintain an influence over the animals. Camels' social hierarchy resembles that of horses, which permitted human control over camels to be developed in a similar sort of way.

The breeding male, keeping to the rear of the herd, holds sway over the females. In a camel caravan the females and their riders go first while the human leader rides the dominant male, which pushes the herd from behind. This male camel periodically calls to the females to keep them together.

Camel caravans tend to keep to regular routes across the desert. The camels soon learn these: they have an exceptional homing skill and, when lost, they have been known to return to their birthplace from a distance of thousands of kilometres. They are also phenomenally sensitive to the proximity of water and can sense it from over 40 kilometres away. Camels owe this ability to their sense of smell and will turn to face in the direction of falling rain even if it is far from sight.

Although the Taureg may use camels to help guide them to water, more often the camels rely on humans to draw water for them from desert wells. In this way the humans deliver their side of the bargain and through this access to water camels are able to exist in areas of the desert that would originally have been inaccessible to them. Humans also supply the camels with another valued commodity – salt. Without this vital mineral the camels rapidly become ill. Camels were originally believed to have been domesticated by lures of salty dried shark and sardines. Fearing few predators, they would have been easy to tame.

The one-humped dromedary camel was domesticated in southern Arabia around 5000 years ago, at about the same time that the Bactrian camel was being separately tamed in southern Russia and Iran. Once the partnership with the dromedary developed it spread from Arabia into Palestine, Syria and the Egyptian Eastern Desert. Its greatest population expansion occurred through the Moslem conquests of Egypt, 1300 years ago. For the Bactrian the relationship proved equally productive and camels spread from southern Russia into western Siberia and China.

If the dromedary had not entered this alliance it would probably now be extinct as the original wild herds no longer exist. The wild Bactrian camel has been reduced to a few groups in remote areas of Mongolia. In South America, meanwhile, the camel's New World relatives still survive. One of them was domesticated at about the same time as the camel.

LLAMA AT THE ALTAR

THE MAIN NEW WORLD CAMELID is known as the guanaco. Its natural home extends from the centre of Peru down to the tip of Tierra del Fuego. Although originally hunted, around 6000 years ago, in an area of natural pasturage in the Lake Titicaca basin of southern Peru, the relationship with humans began to change to that of herding. As a result of domestication two different varieties developed. They were both inefficient at converting herbage into meat so the alpaca became primarily a source of wool while the llama was used for transport.

In Bolivia the Quechua Indians still keep llamas in the traditional manner and they are a central part of these people's religious and social life. Each day the herds are led out of the corrals to feed on the sparse and fibrous vegetation of the mountain grasslands. In natural guanaco herds, a male will lead several females with their young. Here, the llamas are led by a Quechua Indian woman, often spinning wool as she takes them to pasture.

Sometimes their daily treks end up at another village and, as the llamas enter the compound, they may encounter a bizarre and unexpected human scene. While some men lift trays of incense into the air, others dance wildly to the tune of Peruvian pipes and still others swig liquid from earthen jars. These llamas have been invited to a wedding.

The confused and reluctant animals are coerced into socialising. People loom out of the crowd and leer towards them, planting a kiss on their hairy and pliant lips. Sometimes the humans fail to make contact and collapse comatose in front of them. Others pick up the llamas and, holding them in their arms, stagger arhythmically in an uncoordinated attempt at dancing.

The Indians have been imbibing a traditional spirit made from corn. Their drunken revelry and the llamas' participation has a religious purpose. Eventually, one of the llamas is given intoxicating coca leaves to eat and the

*Llamas are still involved in the religious and social life
of the Quechua Indians. This llama is attending
a wedding.*

rest of the llama guests are led away. The remaining sedated llama is then
sacrificed using a knife that is quickly and humanely passed through its brain.
This spilling of blood is considered necessary for a successful wedding.

Such is the interdependence between these people and their herds that
similar festivals, with the participation of the llamas, are enacted at other
important times in the Indians' lives. The Imara Indians, who live in the
same region, have developed an even closer relationship with another animal.
It is the only rodent domesticated in antiquity and still lives in their homes.

KITCHEN CUYS

PERUVIAN INDIANS SHARE THEIR kitchens with colonies of animals
known locally as cuys. These engaging rodents, about the size of a large rat,
come in a variety of colours and coat designs. Some are chocolate brown,
some are piebald white, and others have spectacular rosettes of hair that give
them the appearance of very shaggy Muppets. They can only survive at this

cold altitude because the kitchen fire provides artificial warmth.

As they huddle round the stove, wisps of smoke swirl around them, but they appreciate this because the smoke fumigates their parasites. As their human partners prepare vegetables in a stew pot, the smoky sauna is replaced by steam. Indians believe that the steam is absorbed into the cuys' skin, as they are never seen to drink – in reality they gain all the water they need from their food. Food is something they are certainly never short of. The kitchen provides an endless supply of scraps and, when the cooks are distracted, the cuys supplement this diet by surreptitious raids on the vegetables.

The cuys are regarded highly by the Indians and are featured in myths and legends as well as being credited with powers of divination. They are believed to detect imminent changes in the weather and are thought capable of warding off thunderstorms with their calls.

These highly sociable animals have over 20 communication calls and the Indians have ascribed meanings to many of them. One is thought to warn of approaching strangers. This may be more than an old wives' tale for a cuy's hearing is tuned to a different sound world from that of their human landladies. Deaf to low-frequency sound but aware of ultrasound beyond the range of human hearing, this auditory bias may detect the rustle of approaching footsteps before they are audible to people.

Because of the cuy's prolific nature each home usually keeps only one breeding male. Each female has four or five litters a year, with up to seven young in each and the numbers soon grow until the cuys are literally under everyone's feet. This population explosion is timed to coincide with traditional feast days, which are now clustered around the Christian festival of Christmas.

In this instance, feast day means exactly what it says and the festivals reduce the kitchen cuy population to just two or three individuals. Although cuys can live over five years, most survive less than 12 months before they are eaten. Although this might seem a short existence, the life expectancy of similar rodents in the wild is actually far less and the majority of domesticated cuys are able produce several litters in their lifetimes.

This relationship began between 6000 and 9000 years ago when the people in the region first began to farm. The cuys were probably attracted to villages by the stored products of the emergent agriculture. Once they entered the home they were encouraged to stay.

Although living relatives still exist throughout South America, all traces of the wild ancestor of the cuy have been lost. It is such an engaging animal it has even entered the homes of people living in industrialised countries. Not in the kitchen but in the far less stimulating environment of a hutch. Kept simply as a pet it is more commonly known as a guinea pig.

PAMPERED PETS

SMALL ANIMALS LIKE GUINEA pigs are usually kept by children. This desire to care for tiny, defenceless animals is a kind of rehearsal for parenthood. The same happens in many tribal cultures when the young of a hunted animal is brought back to camp. South American Indians often give baby monkeys to their children to look after just as urban dwellers give their children pet hamsters or gerbils.

The golden hamster's popularity as a pet transformed it from a scarce inhabitant of the steppes of Syria and Southern Turkey to a common animal in homes around the world. Remarkably, all domesticated hamsters are derived from one female and her eight young that were unearthed by a scientist from a field in Aleppo, Syria, in 1930. They bred so well in captivity and were so appealing that they soon became adopted by generations of children. These small pets are especially favoured as they appear vulnerable and unthreatening, but the relationship is inevitably limited as little communication is possible between the animal and its young keeper.

Adults generally prefer to share their home with more responsive creatures and this is why cats and dogs are so popular as human companions. Animals performing this type of role are not unique to Western cultures. The Arara Indians are accompanied everywhere by capuchin monkeys perched on their shoulders. The monkeys' only function is as constant companions.

The understanding that people in the industrialised world develop with their pet is the closest they ever get to communicating with another type of animal. The depth of the relationship is similar to that experienced by people who still live closely with their livestock.

But in industrialised societies pets are regarded totally differently from the domesticated animals that supply humans with meat and even pet food. These companion animals are often treated with total indulgence and, in societies otherwise divorced from the natural world, it is perhaps inevitable that misunderstandings often arise in the relationships.

CAT AMONGST THE HUMANS

CATS HAVE BEEN ASSOCIATING with people since agriculture began in the Fertile Crescent. Attracted to the colonies of mice that plagued the ancient granaries, the cat was tolerated and then encouraged. By Egyptian times it had come to be revered.

Like other domesticated animals, cats' natural behaviour predisposes them to life with humans. They naturally display a strong attachment to a

*Like children around the world, those of the Yanomani Indians
are avid pet-keepers. Here their companions are marsupial rats.*

particular area and so faithfully return to the same home. They are hygienic
and deposit urine and faeces away from the den area. Although basically
solitary they will establish relationships with other cats. This affection can
be directed towards humans but the signals they give to us are not always
correctly understood.

As a feline enters the house through the cat-flap it calls out to a human
with the same soft cheep it uses to greet other cats. It holds its tail vertically,
with the tip curled over as a sign of acceptance. As it meets, it rubs its head
on the person's leg. This apparent display of affection deposits on the leg an

odour from scent glands studded around the cat's mouth and face. It would prefer to rub the head but the difference in size makes this impossible. When it greets other cats in this way it reinforces the odour bond between them.

If a cat is really pleased to see its owner it will roll over on its back in the same display a female uses when trying to solicit attentions from a male. In an unneutered female such displays can become intense and the even the sound of her owner's voice may cause her to crouch down, raise her back in the air and begin to paddle with her back feet. Humans usually interpret this invitation to mount as a desire to be stroked.

Such sexual misdirection is an inevitable consequence of the imprinting that occurs through human rearing. However, most responses have no sexual meaning, for the cat also regards its owner as its mother. Because humans continue their maternal devotion after the kitten has become an adult, the cat retains its kittenish behaviour. A stroking human hand continues to substitute for the cleansing caress of the mother's tongue. In ecstasy, the cat often responds by kneading and dribbling – the same actions that once stimulated the flow of milk from its mother's teats.

Cats react to humans as they would to other cats and they often find a room filled with unfamiliar people an intimidating experience. The cat looks for signs of acceptance. People who gaze on it affectionately are often misunderstood, as such a look has a different meaning in cat society. A direct stare is interpreted as a threat and the cat attempts to lessen the conflict by narrowing its eyes and looking away. Humans fail to respond with the same eye-narrowing signals and, unfortunately, the most ardent cat-lovers tend to send out the most aggressive stares. Only those people who dislike cats deliberately avoid eye contact and this is why their laps are usually favoured.

LEADER OF THE PACK?

ALTHOUGH HUMANS HAVE BEEN associating with dogs for even longer than with cats, communication between them is just as prone to mis-understanding. While a person uses human words to communicate with the dog, it responds with the communication signals of the wild wolf pack. A dog's greeting is generally more exuberant than that of the cat and often a large dog will even jump up to lick its owner's face. In the wolf pack this apparently affectionate kiss is used to elicit the regurgitation of food from a returning animal.

If the dog is truly delighted to see its owner it rolls over on its back and exposes its belly. This is the same puppy posture that once encouraged the mother to clean its genital region with her tongue. The same position is used among adult wolves to signify extreme submission. It is this tendency towards affection and submission that enabled the dog to be successfully integrated into human society.

A dog owner substitutes for the alpha male of the wolf pack and receives the same submissive signals when the dog does something of which the owner disapproves. A dog learns to recognise the human sounds and gestures that signal anger and, if caught stealing food or making a mess on the carpet, it reacts to the wrath by averting its eyes, lowering its head, flattening its fur and at the same time dropping its tail between its legs. Humans interpret this hang-dog expression as a sign of guilt but the dog is really displaying the same signals that, in the wolf pack, discourage an aggressive reaction.

Wolves interpret a direct stare as an aggressive challenge and, like cats, they avoid conflict by averting their eyes. The lowered body is also a submissive posture, which is reinforced by the tail between the legs. As well as being a visual signal, this also reduces the threat by cutting off scent from the anal region. Although the dog's signals are designed to pacify wolves, there are enough similarities with human submissive behaviour to evoke a similar reaction in humans.

Problems arise when the dog gains the impression that it is the dominant member of the human pack. This can happen when people pamper their pets. In nature such privileged treatment is reserved for the dominant pack members and the dog responds by assuming this status. This can result in dogs as small as a Pekinese terrorising their owners and even barring their entrance to certain rooms in the house. Most dog behaviourial problems originate from this kind of misunderstanding of their position in human society. Fortunately, the majority of dogs quite happily fulfil their role as submissive pack members.

Dogs have been living closely with people since they first hunted alongside them and scavenged around their campfires. Across Asia and the Far East dogs still continue to act as scavengers. The pariah dogs of India, the feral dogs of Egypt and Africa, and the village dogs of Bali, still fulfil this role of refuse collectors and are tolerated around human abodes. These dogs live alongside people and act submissively to them but are never pampered or petted. It is in the industrialised world that dogs have become such an important part of many people's lives. These societies now have little contact with other animals and their pets appear to act as a substitute for this natural relationship. Nearly a quarter of all British families care for a dog and 48 million of these animals live in North American homes. In Europe a half of all homes are shared with some kind of pet. Most of these pets live in relative comfort, fed on expensive food and showered with affection.

Because people share their lives with these animals they have an opportunity to communicate directly with them. Even though misunderstandings may arise, the owners understand that each animal has its own personality and requirements and generally attempt to cater for these individual needs. This empathy is an inevitable consequence of living alongside them. In other cultures the same kind of sensitivity develops among people who live with the animals they keep for meat. The relationship we have with our dogs has its counterpart in the way pigs are kept in Papua New Guinea.

PERSONALISED PIGS

PIGS ARE JUST AS INTELLIGENT as dogs and, as the Hagerhai discovered, they too possess many natural characteristics that allow them to fit into human society. They are highly social animals and, like people, they enjoy the bodily contact arising from living within a family group. In addition, their omnivorous nature allows them to eat the same food as people.

Their similarities with humans extend even to sharing a sex hormone, androsterone, which is found both in male human sweat and in large quantities in the saliva of boars. In men the scent has been implicated as having a regulatory effect on the monthly cycle of women. Among pigs it acts as a powerful aphrodisiac. Further, because of their long association with people, pigs also have parasites in common, including the human flea.

Pigs were among the first animals to be domesticated and were attracted to human settlements in the Fertile Crescent 9000 years ago, but such was their affinity to people that they came to share their lives wherever human and pig societies were found together.

Among the settled agricultural tribes of the Papua New Guinea highlands, such as the Huli Wigmen, pig rearing is a central part of their culture. The pigs are used as a symbol of wealth and as a form of barter. Adult pigs are kept on leads like dogs and accompany the women wherever they go. Each day they escort the women to their gardens. As the women dig the soil the pigs do the same with their snouts.

In the evening the pigs return enthusiastically to the comfort of the house. The Huli women live apart from their husbands – they share their communal home with the pigs. Like dogs, the pigs will take up the prime spots by the fire. They are given titbits to eat and petted with great affection. The pigs place their heads comfortably on the women's laps and lie back ecstatically as they are scratched behind the ear or stroked. They enjoy a life as luxurious as that of any dog in Europe or America but there is one profound difference. Eventually they will be killed for meat. This event takes place on special festival days and, as with the Hagerhai and their wild-caught pigs, the women will grieve their loss in the same way that dog-owners react to the death of the family dog.

In India pariah dogs fulfil the useful role of scavengers. They settle their own social disputes without human intervention.

Industrialised societies avoid the agony inevitably involved in killing their food animals by keeping them apart from the people who eat them. The drive to provide more meat for an expanding human population has caused the most cost-effective rearing methods to be employed. This has been at the expense of the animals involved. As no empathy ever develops between these animals and the people that eat them, there is only limited concern over the way they are kept. Consequently, the intelligent and responsive pig is reared as though it is a component in a food-producing machine. The contrast with the lives of Papua New Guinea pigs could not be greater.

PORK MACHINES

PIGS ARE GENERALLY CLEAN animals and naturally deposit their faeces in special latrines but, confined in the pens of intensive farms, they have no choice but to defecate where they stand. To ease cleaning, the pigs are kept on concreted or slatted floors. The pig's sensitive snout is so strongly endowed

In Papua New Guinea the tribes allow their domesticated pigs to carry out every aspect of their natural behaviour. Pigs act as living ploughs as they root around for earthworms. When they are about to give birth they are often helped to build their spectacular domed nests and the young are kept with the mother until they are weaned.

with nerve endings that it can create a mental image of an object simply by touching it with this organ. Here its only contact is with concrete or steel.

In Papua New Guinea, the pigs forage freely and they spend most of the day snuffling with their snouts for earthworms and roots. This behaviour is fundamental to the life of a pig. Under factory farming conditions food arrives in the trough at timed intervals as a monotonous slurry.

Even the act of reproduction allows no room for natural behaviour. The boar's lip glands release a scent that causes the sow to become receptive. In the intensive farm the scent is sprayed on the female with an aerosol and she is usually inseminated artificially. In Papua New Guinea the sow is allowed to mate naturally and, most important of all, as farrowing time approaches she is permitted to prepare for the birth of her offspring.

The sow constructs an elaborate nest of leaf litter and dried grasses, often with a domed roof. Her owner encourages her by providing nesting material and may even help the animal as she starts to construct the nest. In the intensive farm, a week before she gives birth, the sow is herded into a farrowing crate inside which she cannot even turn around. Her sensitive snout vainly searches the concrete floor for nesting material.

When her young are born, the sow cannot turn to touch them. Although the newborn piglets are free to suckle her, bars prevent her from approaching them. In case she crushes them when she lies down, the piglets are lured away from her by a heat lamp that provides an alternative source of warmth. On some farms, each time the sow stands up, cold air is automatically blasted onto the piglets to keep them away from her.

In Papua New Guinea, although the sow and the piglets are never separated, accidents are extremely rare as the mother's natural protective instincts ensure she takes care before she lies down. The only behaviour that the pig in the two environments share is that they both control the amount of suckling by calling to piglets at the times they are producing milk.

Piglets born in Papua New Guinea stay with their mother until they reach an independent age or are nursed by human foster parents. In the intensive farm the young may be separated within a couple of weeks of birth or even after a few hours. Soon after birth, their teeth are clipped and their tails docked to prevent injuries in the fights that continually erupt in the limited confines of their crates. Eventually the piglets are herded together and reared separately from their mothers. Most never see daylight.

It is only recently that this way of rearing pigs has been recognised as being cruel, and in Britain plans are being made to phase out the practice of tethering sows in their stalls. But even when all the proposed changes have been carried out, the lives of pigs in factory farms will still be grossly inadequate compared with those raised in Papua New Guinea.

*In the industrialised world the intelligent and responsive pig is
now reared as if a component in the food-producing machine.*

END OF A PARTNERSHIP

THE WAY LIVESTOCK IS KEPT in Papua New Guinea is not unique.
Nomads and pastoralists still maintain close bonds with their animals, understand their natural requirements and allow them to express their normal
behaviour patterns. Such sympathetic attitudes were essential to the early
stages of domestication. Only when animals became separated from the
people they fed did the relationship shift from that of benign partnership to
one of exploitation.

The majority of people now live in cities and have little contact with
any other animals. The few species that live in our homes are showered with
affection and often live in inappropriate luxury, while those that supply us
with food are treated as little more than machines. Only people who still live
physically close to their livestock avoid this double standard. Their food
animals are treated with the respect we reserve for our pets. The relationship
is practical and caring but devoid of exaggerated sentimentality. It reflects
the partnership that all domesticated animals once had with humans.

As the process of domestication changed people's lives and affected their
attitude to the life around them, it had a corresponding influence on the
development of cultural and religious beliefs. These emerging religions
differed profoundly in the way they regarded plants and animals.

CHAPTER
4

LIFE AND SOUL

As WITH LIONS AND GAME animals on the African savannah today, the lives of our ancestors were intimately entwined with the creatures on which they depended for food. For most of the time they simply coexisted. The prey animals would flee only if the hunters came too close or showed, by changes in their actions, that they were interested in hunting.

But in some ways these predators were different. They not only walked on two legs, but their behaviour was unpredictable. Unlike lions and leopards, which followed regular hunting patterns, the human hunters used subtle methods, like hidden snares and pitfall traps, that outwitted the animals' natural defences. They even made weapons, such as spears, that could bridge the animals' normal flight distance.

What gave these early people an advantage was a brain that could reason. They applied this power of conceptual thought not just to hunting, but towards understanding their relationships with the animals and plants around them. Such contemplation eventually developed into a range of sophisticated religious systems that vary fundamentally in their approach to the natural world. However, what our distant ancestors originally believed about other forms of life can be surmised from the attitudes of hunting people in the present day.

THE BUSHMEN'S BELIEF

DEEP IN THE KALAHARI DESERT the silence of the night is sometimes broken by the chants of dancing Bushmen. These nomadic hunters are drawn together whenever their relationship with the natural world appears to have gone awry – this manifests itself perhaps as illness or a shortage of game.

Flying foxes circle round a Buddha image in a temple sanctuary in Thailand.

Bushmen use trance dancing to make contact with the spirits
they believe inhabit the life around them. They hope to gain
influence over forces normally beyond their control.

They are not alone. The sights and sounds of their primal ceremony reach other desert-dwellers. Each perceives a different aspect of the scene.

Through the supersensitive eyes of a barking gecko the firelit ritual flickers with the intensity of an arc light. Seen from the distance of the gecko's protective burrow, the dancing human shapes appear strangely out of focus. Its burrow does peculiar things to the sound. Designed to amplify the gecko's own calls, it has the same effect on the chanting, which resonates in the burrow at this selected frequency. The strange phenomenon is enhanced by the gecko's own selective hearing.

An owl viewing the scene gains a different impression. Its sight and hearing are acute. It can pinpoint every nuance of the chanting with greater accuracy than any other animal. Its eyes pierce the darkness. Even the dancers in the shadows appear as clear as in daylight.

The flickering firelight attracts other animals too. Moths mistake the fire for moonlight and, as they try to navigate by its erratic beams, are drawn perilously close. Their compound eyes are even more sensitive to light than the owl's but gather only a crude impression of shapes and movement.

Like many of the animals that share the Bushmen's lives, the praying mantis holds a special place in legend. It is believed to be a manifestation of Giiawama, a god responsible for life's practical jokes. This trickster god can appear in any guise at any time or place but its favourite form is the praying mantis. Although it may not be responsible for life's misfortunes, the mantis does indeed have mysterious powers. Using organs on its abdomen known as cerci it can sense from many metres away the air currents created by the Bushmen's gyrations.

Each of these animal views provides a different interpretation of reality. Some improve on human perception and some even discern energies that we cannot detect. Bushmen have a sympathetic knowledge of many of the plants and animals around them and they are only too aware that many of these possess special powers. A desire to contact mysterious forces draws the Bushmen together. They wish to enter the world of spirits.

As they dance, the hypnotic rhythm, stressed by clapping and the stamping of feet, begins to affect their consciousness. Soon they enter a trance. They believe that in this altered mental state they leave their earthly bodies and travel into another realm, where they make contact with the spirits in the life around them. They enter a different reality – one that brings them closer to the natural world and ultimately allows them to influence forces normally beyond their control.

SHAMAN SHADES

MANY HUNTING PEOPLE BELIEVE they can make this journey. Among Bushmen the voyage is available to anyone but most other hunting groups rely on individuals with special powers. These are known as shamans.

Shamanist beliefs were once prevalent throughout the world. They still survive in parts of Siberia, North America, the Arctic, Indonesia and many other areas of South-east Asia. Shamans are expected to secure good weather and drive away evil spirits, particularly those causing sickness. They are particularly important to hunting societies because of the need to contact the spirits of their game.

Hunters are only too aware of the powers of their prey. Using smell, antelopes or deer can sense an approaching human long before they are seen and, through fleetness of foot, effortlessly outpace them in a chase. Eagles or buzzards not only soar away from danger but their superior vision allows them to gaze down on the hunters from invisible heights.

As well as possessing extraordinary sensory and physical abilities these animals also exercise a kind of free will. Whether they stay near the hunters or go elsewhere is totally their decision. It is the shaman's role to gain influence over these powerful and independent creatures.

As well as dancing and chanting, the shaman may use sensory deprivation, fasting and drum-beating to induce the altered states of consciousness necessary for the journey. Hallucinogenic plants such as peyote, psilocybe mushrooms and morning glory achieve the same effect.

Shamans believe that they are transported into the physical body of an animal. Bushmen may turn into elands, springbok or lions, North American Chukchee and Eskimo shamans change into wolves, Lapps become bears or reindeer and the Semang shamans of Malaysia transform themselves into tigers. While in a trance they often imitate the movements and calls of the appropriate animals.

The use of shamans is so prevalent among hunting groups today, it is likely that they were just as important to prehistoric hunting societies. These people must have shared many other beliefs with present-day hunters.

TOTEM AND TABOO

THE DETAILS OF THEIR BELIEFS may vary, but hunters share an extraordinary similarity in their attitude to the life around them. Although they see obvious differences between humans and other animals, they are also aware that there is an intense affinity between them. Daily experience confirms to them that human life is simply an extension of the natural world and this gives rise to almost universal feelings of equality with it. Consequently hunters never consider that they dominate the creatures they hunt.

As they identify so closely with animals, special rites are usually observed in hunting. It is believed that without these the animal will not present itself for sacrifice. Once the animal has been killed it is common for rituals to be enacted to appease the animal spirits.

Some hunters feel such strong links with other life that plants, animals and forces of nature become specifically identified with different human groups. These are adopted as tribal emblems or totems.

Totems are common among North American and other tribal societies but are especially significant among Australian aborigines. Members of each clan call themselves by an animal's name and believe they share a common ancestry. This is more than kinship. The aborigines feel that, as well as being human, they are the totemic animal. Living representatives are only one expression of the totem for it is really a force that lives before and after death. When not in bodily form it resides in the land.

Although the members of each clan hold a taboo against eating their own totemic animal, they will participate in ritualised dancing to increase its supply for the benefit of other clans.

The bee is the totem of the Bawinanga clan. As well as being linked spiritually with the bee, the aborigines are also practically involved with its life. The bees guide them to honey. The aborigines attract the foraging bees by cutting a tree to release syrupy sap. Then a pennant, created from a rolled wad of spider's silk, is attached to the bee's abdomen. The bee navigates back to the hive following a map formed from patterns of polarised light in the sky. These are invisible to human eyes but the spider's silk allows the aborigines to keep sight of the bee and track it back to the hive.

Our hunting ancestors must have had many such close associations with other animals. These began to disappear when people forged new relationships with plants. The changes brought about by agriculture caused corresponding shifts in attitude. Human lives were no longer controlled by independent wild animals – instead they were linked to the success or failure of the harvest. As a consequence religious ideas became directed towards the crop itself.

THE SPIRIT OF THE CROP

CENTRAL TO EARLY AGRICULTURAL religion was belief in a spirit enshrined within the crop. All the main crop-growing areas of the world shared the view that this spirit was represented by a mother figure that inhabited the crop and made it grow. In most places she was believed to reside in the last handful of the harvest. This last sheath was accorded special significance. It was often woven into human form and even dressed in women's clothes – the corn dollies still found in parts of Europe are a legacy of this tradition. South and North America have their counterparts with corn mothers and South-east Asia has a rice mother.

The culture of Bali still revolves around a single staple crop – rice – and has maintained many of its ancient beliefs. These include the idea of a spirit in the rice.

The Balinese treat the divine rice plant as a human entity. Its cultivation is imbued with rituals that emphasise the plant's human qualities. Offerings are made at germination and also forty days afterwards when the seedlings are planted out in the fields. Two days later the rice celebrates its first birthday, bamboo shrines are erected for offerings and three days of festivities begin in the village temple. The rice plants are then allowed three days' rest and for the next thirty days drums are beaten through the streets of the village to invite in the essence that brings the fruit of the crop.

Blooming is considered the most important stage of growth. The rice is now regarded as pregnant and offerings of food considered desirable by pregnant women are placed on the shrines. Rice stalks are woven into human forms and placed at the corners of the fields. These are believed to contain the spirit of the rice.

As the crop ripens it becomes vulnerable. The people are now fully employed in scaring away the swirling flocks of mannikin finches that descend on it. They also have to cope with attacks from mice and rats. Because of the risk to the sacred rice, animals are regarded as a threat so, instead of being revered, they are treated as representatives of evil. Sacrificial rites are thought necessary to appease the demon spirits that control them. Cockfights take place in the temples and the spilt blood is believed to ensure a successful harvest.

Further rituals accompany harvesting. The first bundle of gathered rice is believed to capture the spirit of the crop and, woven into a human form, it becomes the rice mother or Nini. She watches over the gathering of the rest of the crop from a shrine in the corner of the field.

Rice, water and the island's volcanoes form the main focus of Balinese religion. Everyday life is interwoven by a whole system of obligations towards gods, ancestral souls, demons, fellow human beings and the forces of nature. The outcome of life depends on whether people maintain a harmonious balance with all these influences. Each day every Balinese puts offerings of rice and flowers on banana leaf plates to appease these spirits. Offerings to good spirits are placed on altars in the household temple, while those aimed at exorcising evil spirits are left on the ground outside every house.

Dogs observe these rituals with interest and several of these free-ranging animals adopt each Balinese family. They learn at an early age that the outside offerings constitute a reliable meal, so these are devoured as soon as they reach the ground. Such behaviour is regarded as perfectly in order. Dogs are considered lowly so have links with the world of evil spirits.

The Balinese hold all animals in similarly low esteem and rituals serve to emphasise their separation from humans. Babies are not allowed to crawl on the floor on all fours and are carried until they can walk. At puberty children even have their canine teeth filed down to stress their non-animal natures. In contrast, plant life, because it is so central to existence in Bali, is elevated to the highest level. Nevertheless, animals that actually inhabit temples are held in respect.

Opposite above: Dogs watch with interest as a Balinese girl makes her daily offering to appease evil spirits.
Opposite below: In Bali, when the rice matures, it is presented with offerings of food that would be considered desirable by pregnant women.

BALINESE BAT TEMPLE

THE WALLS OF THE cave temple at Goa Lawah are black with the bodies of rousettus fruit bats. It is a scene of continual loud activity. As bats squabble for prime roost-sites in the interior of the cave they produce a chattering din. Remarkably, the sound is made by the bat clicking its tongue: the tongue-clicks are used to create pictures in sound. The clicks reverberate off the cave walls and the bats use this echolocation technique to gain an impression of their surroundings. As the bats fly about trying to improve their foothold, their sound images are often of processions of people going to the temple.

This temple is considered an auspicious site as the cave is believed to reach the base of Gunung Agung, the holiest volcano on the island. Because of this the bats are protected and show little fear of the human pilgrims. They even mate and give birth while the ceremonies continue below them. The only danger to the bats comes from the poisonous snakes that hunt in the cave. These are also considered sacred by the Balinese and in fact held in even greater esteem.

Other temples on the island act as refuges for monkeys. This respect for temple animals, which contrasts with the general Balinese attitude to animal life, stems from the influence of another religion, which reached the island between the eighth and fifteenth centuries AD. Culturally malleable, it readily melted into the traditional system of beliefs. The religion was Hinduism and its origins lay in India.

CYCLES OF REBIRTH

THE ROOTS OF HINDUISM can be traced to the early Indus valley civilisation between 5000 and 7000 years ago. The original Vedic religion arose as local tribes came together to create a new culture and evolved as the various localised beliefs began to merge and blend. This eventually led to the development of Hinduism, which today incorporates a rich variety of teachings and practices.

Among this diversity, Hindus share a common belief in an all-pervading God and in the endless cycle of birth and rebirth of each soul. The soul is carried in its earthly form either as a human or as another animal. Individuals traverse endless time through a succession of rebirths and can be born as animals or into various human castes. Their ultimate destiny is shaped by the deeds they perform in life. Final release from the cycles of reincarnation is won through the karma acquired by meritorious acts and through the gaining of a superior insight into the nature of the universe. Only then does the soul reach nirvana and achieve unity with God.

*The Balinese Hindu temple of Goa Lawah provides sanctuary
for thousands of sacred fruit bats.*

Brahma, Vishnu and Shiva are the most important of the 330 million
gods of classical Hinduism but all are believed to be manifestations of the
one God. How each is represented varies with the different social traditions
of the people. A community of Hindus usually shows a special attachment
to a particular god and, as the gods are often represented in animal form,
the corresponding living animals are held in particular esteem.

RAT RELATIVES

AS NIGHT FALLS IN Deshnok, in the Indian province of Rajasthan, a priest carrying a flaming torch, fuelled by melted butter, enters the inner sanctum of the village temple. Accompanied by the clanging rhythm of an ancient mechanical music-maker and the chants of pilgrims, he raises a shroud of muslin in front of the flames. Ghostly silhouettes appear on the diaphanous cloth and as these spectral outlines dance and shimmer they eventually coalesce to form the unmistakeable shapes of rats.

This nightly service or puja is dedicated to the goddess Karniji. The rats, invited to attend with the offer of food, are believed to be living representatives of her relatives and are known as kabas. The inner sanctum was built for Karniji and her kabas in the sixteenth century but in the nineteenth century the temple was expanded and elaborated. Its marble-lined walls were even constructed with Tom-and-Jerry style mouseholes included in the design. The fortunate inhabitants of this palace are black rats and for the past four hundred years countless generations have lived a sumptuous existence within its elegant confines.

All predators are excluded – even the courtyard is covered with wire to prevent attacks from hawks and falcons. Consequently the rat population reaches thousands and death comes only through disease or old age. Protected from the pressures that limit them in the wild, the rats have shown remarkable modifications to their behaviour.

Wild rats instinctively avoid new objects and this neophobia makes them difficult to trap. Temple rats have no such inhibitions and swarm excitedly over baskets, bags and even human feet as soon as these touch the ground. Wild rats feel secure only when their bodies are in contact with objects, this thigmotaxis ensuring that they make their runs along walls. Temple rats show no such preference and, protected from danger, happily cross open spaces. Even more remarkably, the temple rats have given up their nocturnal way of life and now behave completely naturally in broad daylight.

The maximum size reached by wild rat colonies is around 600 individuals, and after that numbers tend to crash because of disease and stress. In the temple the population is stabilised at about 10 000, though, even at this phenomenally high level, there is little aggression between the rats. Conflicts tend to arise from sexual competition, and most males show signs of injuries from this type of sparring. Encounters between males often result

In Deshnok temple in India a devotee of Karniji meditates in the company of black rats.

For the devout, sharing food with the temple rats is like sharing it with a relative. Ten thousand rats survive on the offerings presented by worshippers.

in stylised boxing matches: the rats raise themselves up on their back legs and let loose a flurry of pulled punches and kung fu style kicks. A female on heat may attract a pursuing retinue of up to 15 males. As, in the resulting chase, the rats skid across the marbled floor, human visitors frequently become involved. The rats show no fear of people and readily make use of a leg as a ladder.

Offerings brought by worshippers are donated to the rats, which consequently subsist on a diet mainly of sweets, supplemented by grain given by the priests. Some temple visitors even share their own meals with the rats, eating dhal and rice from the same bowl. From a Western perspective such closeness appears revolting, if not downright dangerous (these are the same species of rat as that responsible for carrying the Black Death) but it seems that this isolated population of rats does not transmit diseases to people. For the devout, such sharing is affirmation of their affinity with the kabas.

The people of Deshnok village think that when they die they will be reincarnated as kabas. Sharing food with them is therefore like eating with friends and relatives. When the kabas die they in turn are reincarnated as people. In this way the villagers feel they have broken out of the endless cycle of death and rebirth that characterises the beliefs of other Hindu sects.

HOLY COWS

COWS ARE REVERED THROUGHOUT India. How they came to be regarded as sacred is uncertain, but the custom is thought to have originated as Indo-European pastoralists migrated down from the north. Like the cattle farmers of Africa, these people had a close relationship with their animals, which eventually became symbols of wealth. As the cow was incorporated into Hindu mythology it came to represent incarnations of the sacred milch cow of heaven. Today some cows are kept to provide the five sacred products – milk, ghee, yoghurt, urine and dung. Others eke out an existence in the streets of cities and villages.

Many Indian cows have become totally urban animals and in towns like Ahmedabad, Gujarat, they pass their whole lives without seeing a blade of grass. They are so accustomed to this lifestyle that they will frequently choose to sleep in the middle of the busiest thoroughfares. Protected by their holy status, they doze contentedly as rickshaws, trucks and motor cars career frantically around them. It is considered extremely inauspicious to kill a cow and so, even in a country with one of the highest rates of vehicle accidents, cow fatalities are extremely rare. The cattle sleep soundly, unaffected by the chaos surrounding them.

These animals play a useful role as garbage collectors, consuming the rubbish straight off the streets. Even newspapers are happily devoured, presenting a challenge to the cellulose-digesting bacteria that inhabit their gut. The cows supplement this uninspiring fare by food raided from stall-holders and shoppers.

The marauding technique has been perfected by the cows that stalk the vegetable markets of Varanasi, Uttar Pradesh. These street-wise animals have given up passive grazing altogether. Instead they actively patrol an area of the market and watch for opportunities to arise. Even devout Hindus cannot let their livelihoods disappear down a cow's throat, so the stallholders arm themselves with wooden staves and keep their guard.

These bovine prowlers have learnt that a surprise attack is best. As soon as a stallholder is distracted the cow makes its move. Without pausing, it swings its head between the shoppers' legs and, with a flowing movement of

*Above: After raiding a market stall, a holy Indian cow finds a
busy street is a pleasant place to chew the cud.
Opposite: Even the devout find their patience tried as their
livelihoods disappear down a cow's throat.*

its long tongue, scoops up a generous mouthful of vegetables. The marauder
is usually halfway across the street before the stallkeeper has time to react.

The cows also make strategic raids on shopping baskets. The technique
involves nonchalantly extending a neck as the basket passes or waiting until
the shopper's back is turned before surreptitiously snaffling the contents.

MONKEY MUGGERS

MONKEYS ALSO TRY THEIR luck with Hindu patience. The monkey god
Hanuman is actually the leaf-eating langur. Hanuman temples may shelter
these playful monkeys but rhesus macaques are more common inhabitants.
They live on the offerings brought for them by the devout.

The legions of monkeys that live in other temples are not so fortunate.

Although protected by their holy status, they are not specifically brought offerings and have to obtain food by pilfering. Monkeys at the Durga temple in Varanasi have perfected the art of the mugger.

Monkeys perched on the entrance porticoes survey each temple visitor. They look for easy targets and single out people who neglect to hide their offerings. Their technique relies on ambush and, as the monkey creeps towards its victim, it uses the temple columns as a screen. When no human eyes are watching it darts forward, either grabbing the offerings from the hand or knocking them into the air with a flying leap. As the packets of sweets or cakes burst open on the ground the monkey stuffs them into its cheek pouches before anyone has time to react.

The macaques are skilled at choosing suitable prey. They prefer women and children, who are less likely to resist. Older monkeys may use direct intimidation and have learnt that a strong hand tugging at a sari is rarely refused. They treat people who deliberately feed them very differently, however, and could not be more delicate as they take the proffered food.

Cows and monkeys push the Hindus' respect for animals to the limit, though the concept of tolerance pervades the whole of Hinduism. However, even with this respect for the natural world, much of India's forests have still been destroyed because of the pressures of overpopulation. Nevertheless, religion was responsible for one of India's earliest nature reserves.

TREE-HUGGERS

THE MEMBERS OF THE Bishnoi sect were among the first conservationists. The movement was founded in the seventeenth century when hundreds of adherents hugged trees to prevent them from being logged. Although the defiance resulted in many of the tree-huggers being murdered, the sect continued. Today they occupy one of the few remaining wooded regions left in Rajasthan. The trees have only survived because of protection from the Bishnoi and the forest now provides sanctuary for the endangered blackbuck antelope. The Bishnoi only use dead wood as fuel and so deep is their respect for other living things they always check the wood to ensure that no insects perish in the fire.

Although Hinduism today is characterised by this regard for animal life, the early Vedic religion placed great emphasis on animal sacrifice. The sacrificial offerings were carried out by people belonging to the priestly class

A garland of flowers makes a welcome change of diet for a temple macaque and her baby.

of Brahmins. Although some Hindu sects, particularly in Nepal, still continue animal sacrifice, the sacrificial idea is now more usually carried out using plants or clarified butter.

The original Vedic scriptures advocate vegetarianism and this is still the practice in the much of the south of India. It was, however, the influence of Jainism and Buddhism that finally shaped the philosophy of non-violence towards other life. These religions emerged around 2500 years ago.

ALL CREATURES GREAT AND SMALL

THE JAINS BELIEVE THAT all animals, plants and natural elements have souls and that all humans have been living things in previous lives. Because of this declared affinity with other organisms, they consider that all life has a right to exist. Three million people still follow these beliefs and practise ahimsa, non-injury to other forms of life.

Not only totally vegetarian, in their daily lives the Jains take great care to avoid causing damage to any animal. Their concern extends even to insects and microscopic entities. They believed in micro-organisms long before they had been discovered by science and are careful to minimise the chances of injuring them.

Jainist monks refuse to wash for fear of harming the micro-organisms on their bodies. They strain their drinking water to avoid gulping down any living creature and one sect, the shvetambaras, wear masks to prevent the accidental killing of airborne insects. They will not eat after sundown as the risk of swallowing night-flying insects is too high. As they walk they brush the ground with peacock feathers to clear away unseen organisms. Before they sit down they carefully dust away the creatures that may be beneath them.

The most extreme group of Jains, the digambaras (sky-clad), will not wear clothes, as an expression of their devotion and to lessen the chance of squashing organisms against the skin.

As in most religions it is only the practising monks that fulfil all the demands of the Jainist doctrine but through their adherence to the most stringent principles they offer an example to others. Lay members are staunch vegetarians and take jobs that minimise the harming of any living thing. Although the actual number of practising Jains is small the religion has helped to influence the whole of Hinduism and has shaped its attitude to other life.

Buddhism, too, encompassed a philosophy of respect for all creatures. This belief system arose in India around the same time.

The nakedness of a Jainist monk helps affirm his belief that he should harm no living thing.

*Above: The snakes that live in a Buddhist temple in Penang
view meditating worshippers through an infra-red sense.
Opposite: Many Buddhist temples in Thailand offer sanctuary
to flying foxes. They are considered symbols of a long life.*

FUNERAL FLIGHT

A BUDDHIST TEMPLE IN Penang, Malaysia, is inhabited by snakes with apparently unearthly powers. As the monks offer up their daily prayers, these creatures are able to see energy emanating from the monks as a ghostly ethereal glow. This seemingly extrasensory view is provided through the snake's pit-organ, which is able to create images from the infra-red heat produced by life processes of warm-blooded animals. Through this sense, used to help it track down living prey, the snake perceives a different reality to that of its human visitors.

As the monks meditate they are trying to understand a world beyond both human and animal perception. As Buddhists they believe that the snakes are connected to humans and all other life by a continuous life-force. In this interpretation of the world there is no individual identity, for all that

exists is linked together by the cycles of birth, growth, decay and death. Life is forever seeking self-expression in new forms. What these forms become depends on the merit gained in previous lives. Animals are held to be lower than humans but the aim of humans is to reach an even higher state. This is the state of nirvana or enlightenment where the mind attains tranquillity and is freed from the endless cycles of rebirth. Because all humans have been animals in previous existences, Buddhists respect all forms of life.

In a previous existence the Buddha was an elephant and this animal is regarded more highly than any other. Consequently many Buddhist temples are decorated with representations of the Hindu elephant god Ganesha. At Wat Ta Sung, near Bangkok, the image of Ganesha flickers in the mid-day sun from the shadows cast by the wings of roosting flying foxes. These large reddish-brown bats fan their cloak-like wings to gain relief from the relentless heat. They are found in many other temple sites throughout Thailand.

Except when disturbed by squabbles over roosting spots, these animals rarely fly in daylight. But there is a spectacular exception. Every few weeks the bats watch as a procession of monks and lay people make their way to the temple. After an hour of prayers and chanting, a lone figure leaves the temple and places a cylinder on the ground and then backs away. Seconds later the cylinder explodes. Like autumn leaves stripped from trees in a gale, bats stream into the air until the blue sky is flickering black with their wing-beats. They circle the temple protesting at the disturbance.

The commotion was caused by a firecracker. Lit at the end of a funeral, it signalled the departure of the life essence from the body. Although an individual had died, the Buddhists believe that there is no real death for the life will continue in the new beings that arise. That the bats should take part in this spectacle is entirely appropriate, as to Buddhists they are symbols of longevity. Different flying creatures, vultures, take an even more active part in the process of death in the mountains of Tibet.

Vultures circle each morning above the temples of remote Tibetan communities to watch the activity of the priests below. They are looking for signs that a human corpse is being prepared. When people die their life essence departs. Their physical remains are cut up and laid out at special sacred sites to offer up flesh to these scavenging birds.

To the Buddhists the vulture is another manifestation of the one force that connects all living things. The interrelationships between life forms are believed to create a complex web which, beyond human understanding, weaves together all being. Because of this belief in the unity of life a profound peception of the significance of nature is common to Buddhism.

As well as sheltering **flying foxes** and attracting vultures, **temple sites** often offer sanctuary to other animals.

A Buddhist monk feeds fish in a river sanctuary outside the
temple of Wat Pal Rong near Bangkok.

ANIMAL SANCTUARIES

AN EAGLE SOARING OVER the lush rice paddies and wheat fields of North-east Thailand is looking down on a landscape that, from the viewpoint of the former animal inhabitants, is a scene of ecological devastation. But, in this agricultural desert, the temple of Wat Pah Ban Taad provides a woodland oasis where the eagle can build a nest and rear its young. The temple grounds also act as a sanctuary for gibbons, flying squirrels and many woodland birds. In Thailand alone about 700 of these forest monasteries provide similar protection for the refugees of deforestation.

As the sun reflects off the gilt decorations of the temple of Wat Phai Lom, not far from Bangkok, thousands of open-billed storks rise up on thermals and spiral above the temple precincts. From this lofty position the trees of the monastery must appear as if covered in snow. Eighty thousand of the storks have made these few acres their home and the sheer numbers of nesting birds turn the tree-tops white.

Although the birds benefit from the snails that inhabit the rice fields, the removal of trees has destroyed most of their former breeding colonies. This temple is one of the few retreats left to them. In a previous life the Buddha appeared as an egret and so these related birds have a special significance to the monks that care for them.

Fish are also protected in some monasteries. To the Buddhist they represent awareness and, compared with humans, they do possess some truly remarkable powers. Along the length of their body a series of sensitive hairs attached to jelly-like rods is buried in a special groove. The purpose of these lateral line organs is to detect the movement of other fish and prey. They are so sensitive they can be used to gain an impression of the fish's surroundings by detecting watery deflections created as the fish swims.

The catfish has extra powers. Its body is covered by so many taste receptors it is effectively a swimming tongue and, like the lateral line system, these additional sensors also pick up water movements. In the river that flows past the temple of Wat Pal Rong, near Bangkok, catfish use both these special senses to find food given to them by monks and visitors to the temple.

The initial signal is the water disturbance created as a lump of bread hits the surface. This is detected by the nearest fish which instantly lunges towards it. The sudden movement immediately attracts other fish which in turn alert others. Within seconds the water is a bubbling cauldron of fish bodies trying to swallow the bread. Buoyed up like a cork and head-butted by the competing fish the bread may last several seconds before it disappears in a gulp down a gaping mouth. When it goes, it vanishes in an instant, for the fish are huge: some are over a metre in length and weigh 7 kilograms.

Such a fish would be a prize catch for any of the local fishermen and in this stretch of river there are not just hundreds but literally thousands of the monsters. But the fishermen never get the chance to try their luck, for the fish have learnt that they are protected here and confine themselves to the stretch of the river immediately in front of the temple. By feeding the fish, visitors show compassion to another living being and in this way gain merit. Unaffected by the apparent inconsistency, the same people are equally likely to buy catfish from the market to eat.

Although the Buddha preached vegetarianism, the tolerance of the religion was such that, as it spread, countries that were traditionally meat-eating retained the carnivorous way of life. The idea of obtaining merit from good deeds to animals was subject to other misinterpretation.

The Buddhist monastery of Wat Phai Lom acts as a sanctuary
for Thailand's diminishing population of open-billed storks.

INSTANT KARMA

IN THE COURTYARD OF the temple of Wat Pho, Bangkok, and in many other Thai temples, are piles of tiny bamboo cages. They imprison hundreds of mannikin finches which, crammed along crowded perches, watch the activity of the worshippers outside. The bustling scene appears entirely alien to them, for these are birds of the rice fields. As they settled in their roost, the night before, they were trapped by a net thrown over them. They were caught simply to be released. Temple visitors pay for the privilege and through the karma of this kind action they hope to gain merit.

The birds are victims of a misinterpretation of the teachings of the Buddha. What started as an altruistic act towards other life has become corrupted into a meaningless ritual. To satisfy the needs of the pious, countless birds are taken from the wild simply to be let go again. Many of them never make it back to their original haunts.

On special festive days people release other captives. Ignorance of the animals' natural requirements means that they are often replaced in entirely the wrong environment. Land tortoises may suddenly find themselves in a river, while gibbons or other wild creatures may be introduced to the trauma of urban Bangkok.

As religions distanced themselves from their beginnings it was inevitable that religious practices became increasingly ritualised. Agriculture intensified and ultimately gave way to spreading urbanisation, so the beliefs became separated from day-to-day living. Even so, Eastern religions have maintained close spiritual links with the animal world and reverence for other life is central to their philosophies. Western religions sprang from similar roots but separation from nature started sooner and became more extreme.

THE NUMINOUS NILE

THE DISPARATE NILE VALLEY tribes that eventually came together in the early Egyptian civilisation shared many of the beliefs of present-day nomadic hunters. Each group was symbolised by a totemic animal. When these hunters settled down to become farmers and herdsmen, these totemic

Acts of kindness towards animals is a way for Buddhists to gain merit. This has been distorted into a meaningless ritual in which birds are caught simply to be released.

animals came to represent gods in their emerging religion. One of the most popular totems was a bull.

By 7000 years ago, this symbol of power and strength had become the bull god Apis, one of the most important deities in the newly unified Egypt. A bull identified as Apis was believed to be the physical representative on earth of the god-of-all-gods Ptah and he took part in fertility ceremonies at the temple. When the bull died he was mummified like a pharaoh and the priest had to scour the land to find a divine replacement. This privileged black calf could be recognised by a selection of special markings, including a white inverted triangle on his brow, a vulture-like patch on his shoulders and a crescent moon on his flank.

The chance of a priest finding an animal bearing the right symbols was helped by the variation created as selective breeding intensified at this time. Among other important signs were a falcon shape on the abdomen and a scarab-shaped mark beneath the tongue. Both these animals had religious significance. The falcon was the symbol of Horus and through its spectacular high flying it became identified with the sun. The scarab beetle was associated with the sun cycle and reincarnation. Its habit of rolling balls of animal dung led to the belief that it rolls the sun's orb across the sky. The scarab buries the dung ball in the ground and lays its eggs inside. The dung ball acts as a food reserve for the developing larvae and, once they have consumed the interior, they pupate inside. The pupae resemble mummified adults. After several months they emerge through the hard walls of the dung sarcophagus and appear on the surface. To the Egyptians this apparently magical process suggested reincarnation.

The Egyptians worshipped many other animal divinities, including the jackal, the hawk, the ram, the vulture and the crocodile. Originally only those animals kept in the temples were regarded as sacred but eventually it was assumed that all members of a species had elements of the divine. Some of these animals were mummified in spectacular numbers. In Saqqara alone 800 000 falcons and four million sacred ibis have been discovered while another site yielded 300 000 mummified cats. Cats were associated with several divinities, including Bastet, Sekhmet and Mut. At this time they were proving their practical worth by controlling the burgeoning mouse populations of the Egyptian granaries. They were often kept as pets and when one died the family would shave their eyebrows and go into mourning.

Ordinary Egyptians were forbidden to kill wild animals and for specially sacred animals, such as the falcon and the ibis, the penalty for even accidental killing was death. However, in common with many other early religions, animal sacrifices were believed necessary to satisfy the appetites of the super-natural powers that controlled human destiny.

SACRIFICING REVERENCE

THE CONCEPT OF ANIMAL sacrifice goes back as far as recorded history. It probably originated in the kinship that early men felt with the creatures they hunted. To appease the animals' spirits killing them became imbued with ritual and eventually a belief developed that the gods were pleased by sacrifice. Sacrifice was then used to avert catastrophe or secure success.

Religions that practise animal sacrifice share the same basic rituals. Often the animal is encouraged to appear willing or even happy that it has been selected for such an important role. Only a priest, who has divine sanction and is therefore blameless, is allowed to perform the slaughter. As a result temples became not only places of worship but also abattoirs and butcher shops.

Animal sacrifice was to become the main ritual of both the Greek and Roman religions, which were loosely structured but shared polytheistic beliefs. Sacrifice was used as a way of making contact with the multiple deities. The entrails of the animal victim were read for signs that the gods accepted or rejected the sacrifice. The meat was eaten by those taking part.

Sacrifice continued to be important throughout the Egyptian era. As the civilisation developed, however, the animal gods that were central to the religion became increasingly symbolic and their earthly living representatives were no longer treated with the same reverence, though animals were still regarded as partners. In the societies that grew out of this cultural background, reverence for animal life began to disappear completely.

IN HIS OWN IMAGE

THE ISRAELITES REJECTED THE Egyptian religious system of many gods often appearing in animal guises and replaced it with a belief in a single God, who, significantly, was conceived of in human form. This one God was held to transcend the world and rule over it from above. He was so powerful he was thought to need appeasing with frequent animal sacrifices. These involved slitting the animal's throat on sacrificial altars, then the remains would often be burnt, with the resulting aroma intended to reach God in the sky above.

A major significance of this new religion was its attitude to animal life. For the first time humans were set apart from the rest of the animal kingdom. This change of perspective was reinforced by the connection between the Israelite pastoralists and their herds. By this time, the sheep that mainly constituted their livestock had become subdued and compliant animals. They no longer scattered when herded but instead clumped together, which allowed them to be managed by a human leader, whose authority was readily accepted by the flock. The fact that a shepherd could so easily control the herd reinforced the developing idea of human superiority. The relationship between sheep and shepherd became a useful metaphor for that between people and the new God.

Wild animals were seen as either irrelevant or as competitors. Wild and powerful animal images, such as the lion and the falcon, were replaced by the peaceful and submissive symbols of the domesticated lamb and the dove.

The old Israelite religion formed the basis of Judaism and its sacrificial elements became incorporated into dietary laws which required that food animals were to be ritually slaughtered. To create kosher food forbidden parts of the animal had to be disposed of and the blood removed by salting. There were strictures against eating animals without a cloven hoof and those that did not chew the cud. Birds of prey and sea creatures without fins and scales were also forbidden. Meat and milk could not be cooked or eaten together.

The dietary laws helped impart an element of spirituality to the process of eating animals. They also served to separate the Jews from neighbouring cults and acted as a constant reminder of their unique identity.

Although the Jewish religion supported the notion of people's superiority, it continued to extol the virtue of treating animals, especially domesticated creatures, with compassion.

Islam and Christianity sprang from the same religious roots and shared similar attitudes to animals. The creation stories in Genesis, common to all three religions, emphasised the separation of humans from other creatures. In place of a belief in equality with, and reverence for, other life, the Old Testament emphasised that people were placed in dominion over animals, which had been created to serve human needs.

This feeling of being apart from the natural world was being reinforced by the growing separation of people from the animals and plants around them. The expanding populations were now relying on a few domesticated animals for food and these docile and helpless creatures were so changed from their wild forms that they helped strengthen the view that humans had control over the animal sphere.

Also, the spread of agriculture had transformed the natural landscape and the great majority of people rarely came into direct contact with nature. When they did, it was usually to subdue it and bring it under their control. Physically distanced from the rest of the animal world it became easy for people to believe that they were intrinsically superior to it. However, although both Islam and Christianity emphasised this feeling of separation, like Judaism, they also preached a degree of compassion towards other creatures.

*Like the Bedouin today, the early Israelites were desert
pastoralists who relied on their herds of sheep
and goats.*

KORANIC COMPASSION

ISLAM TEMPERED ITS ENDORSEMENT of human superiority with moral
guidelines on how people should exercise their power. The ritual of animal
sacrifice continued but, as usually happens with this practice, there was an
attempt to minimise distress to the animals involved. To prevent undue
suffering the knife was supposed to be as sharp as possible. It was also
important that the animal should not see the knife being sharpened and that
it was killed out of sight of others.

The Koran preaches that animals should only be used out of necessity
rather than for greed or self-gratification. They should always be treated
with compassion and humility: for example, pack animals are not to be
loaded more than is bearable. All blood sports are condemned. The Koran
even suggests that food and other resources of nature should be shared
equitably with other creatures.

Although the Islamic religion expressly forbade the exploitation of animals, it nevertheless implied that there was a gulf between humans and other life and this perspective allowed a disregard for animals to develop. The same distancing between humans and animals became a feature of the Christian religion.

DOMINATION OR STEWARDSHIP?

WHEN CHRISTIANITY CAME INTO being 2000 years ago the physical separation between people and the natural world was already almost total. The population was sustained by domesticated plants and animals – humans appeared to be in control. The natural world had so little significance that the New Testament makes few references to it. When it does make mention of animals it is usually in the form of metaphors. This indifference to animals was further emphasised by the conviction that they did not possess souls and that humans held dominion over nature.

Whether dominion meant domination or stewardship depended on the prevalent social attitude. It was frequently interpreted as a licence for exploitation. This view was promoted by Saint Thomas Aquinas but other saints dissented. Saint Francis of Assisi was renowned for his benevolence towards animals and members of the Franciscan order preached a love of nature and a humane attitude to other species.

Throughout Europe a tradition of ceremonial blessings of animals have become associated with various saints' days. Each year, horses, mules and assorted pets find themselves in the courtyard of the church of Saint Eusebio in Rome. They are participants in celebrations surrounding the feast day of Saint Anthony, patron and protector of lower animals. At the end of the service they are sprinkled with holy water and sanctified.

Similar festivals are held in other parts of Italy and also in Spain. In France, Camargue sheep which have spent the summer months on the high plateaux of the Dauphiné are herded together for an ancient blessing of the flocks. A similar festival is held at Amélie-les-Bains-Palalda near the Spanish border. Here mules, led through the town by people dressed in traditional Catalonian costume, are accompanied by dancers. The animals are then blessed at the front of the church.

SNAKE SENSATIONS

OF ALL ANIMALS FEATURING in the Christian tradition, the serpent has the most associations with evil. But in Cucullo, in Italy, on San Dominica's day even snakes are blessed. Four-lined and Aesculapian snakes are caught as they emerge from hibernation in the spring. On the first Thursday in May

*On San Dominica's day in Cucullo, Italy, snakes participate
in a Christian festival with its roots in Roman times.*

they are taken from earthenware pots and draped over a statue of the saint
which is carried from the church.

As the statue teeters above the crowd, these tree-dwelling snakes instinctively cling to it. From their perch around the saint's halo the snakes are
alert to the swaying throng below. Their eyes are sensitive to the slightest
movement but, as they can focus only closely, they perceive merely a blurred
image of the procession. They have no true ears, but they are far from deaf.

In Biblical legend the serpent was cast out from the garden of Eden and
forced to crawl on its belly. This position places its whole body in contact
with the ground and allows it to sense groundborne vibrations. Its ribs, and
particularly its jaw, pick up these low-frequency sounds, which are amplified
by the snake's lung. Each time the snake's jaw touches the head of the statue
it hears a sudden roar of distant traffic and the footsteps of the crowd. The
statue acts as a sounding board, amplifying any low, rumbling noises and
every hand that reaches out and touches it transmits even more sound.

As the statue is paraded through the town the snakes' tongues flicker to taste the air. The snake's forked tongue, another potent symbol of evil, is used to gather scent particles and carry them back to a special taste receptor, the Jacobson's organ, at the back of the mouth. These snakes are responding to the smells of the crowd. The odours of mammals signify either food or danger and, as the snakes are carried forward, they try to assess the olfactory information greeting them.

Although this ceremony was Christianised 1000 years ago, its origins date back to Roman times when snakes were revered. The Aesculapian snake included in the festival is associated with Aesculapius, the god of medicine. Participants in the procession still believe that the snakes will protect them from toothache for the rest of the year.

When the snakes return to the church they are placed back in their earthenware pots and later returned to the place they were caught. The pre-Christian roots of this ritual ensure that the snakes are well-treated but in other snake festivals in the Alps and Pyrenees the snake is regarded in its Biblical role as a symbol of evil and at Luchon in the Pyrenees snakes are burnt alive on Saint John's Eve.

RATTLESNAKES IN RHYTHM

IN PARTS OF THE UNITED STATES rattlesnakes have become the subject of another Christian snake cult. Based on an interpretation of a Biblical text that invites believers to take up serpents to prove their faith, this fundamentalist group conducts services that involve the handling of venomous snakes. To the accompaniment of clapping and guitar music the snakes are passed from person to person. As the snake-handlers dance in a jerky rhythm they are trying to demonstrate their belief. Although the snakes are man-handled, they rarely bite, for the experience is strangely confusing for them.

Like the snakes in the temple in Penang, rattlesnakes have a heat-sensitive pit between their eyes and nostrils which can produce a crude image from the infra-red rays emitted by warm-blooded animals. As the snakes are swung in time to the music, they try to make sense of the data assailing them. The soft-focus appearance of the dancers, picked up by the rattlesnake's eyes, is overlaid by the ghostly shimmer of the humans' body heat, gathered by the pit-organ. When the snake strikes at prey or danger it relies on this infra-red view to guide it, but in the crowded chapel these images are overwhelming and, combined with the swaying movements, they cause the snake to become disorientated.

The fundamentalist snake-handlers may seem a long way from traditional Christian practice, but they are driven by a desire to return to the

*In parts of North America fundamentalist snake-handlers
perform frenzied dances with venomous snakes to demonstrate
their Christian faith.*

roots of their religion. The rhythmic dancing creates a trance-like state in which the participants believe they are taken over by the Holy Spirit. Paradoxically, this altered state of consciousness bears similarities to the trance dancing of tribal shamans but, due to their cultural background, the snake-handlers provide a very different interpretation.

Tribal cultures that still live in a world in touch with other life intuitively understand their relationship with it. They realise that they depend on animals and plants for food and sustenance. They kill to eat but respect the life they hunt. As soon as people began to grow crops the process of separation began. Eastern religions have maintained a belief that humanity is a part of nature even when physically isolated from it. Only the West developed a view that the animal sphere was quite distinct.

A look at the life of the human body itself amply confirms that, no matter how far our lives are apparently distanced from the natural world, they are still inescapably part of it.

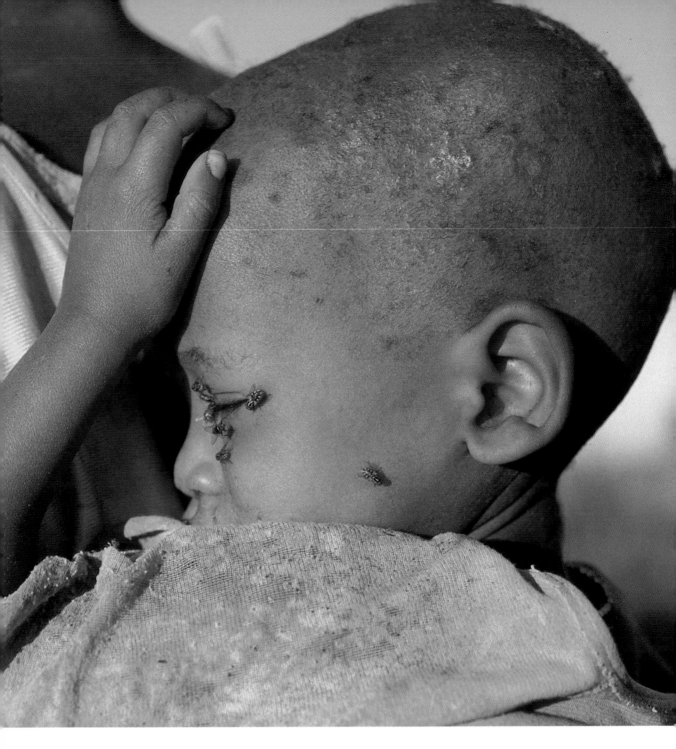

This relative of the housefly has become adapted to feeding from eye and skin secretions.

CHAPTER
5
HUMAN LIFE

O F ALL THE ANIMALS THAT share human lives, none have forged closer links than those that visit us to feed, or spend their lives on or even inside our bodies. Literally millions of these creatures are our constant companions.

To these organisms each person appears like a miniature world. It is an environment consisting of a variety of climatic zones and geographical areas, each with its own specialist fauna and flora. Many places overflow with rich and nutritious food. The most productive regions are the moist tropical forests formed by the hairier parts of our body, the least inhabited are the cold temperate wastes of our exposed limbs. Many creatures are attracted to the vast damp caverns formed by our mouth and other openings, while others squeeze into the fissures at the base of every hair.

The undulating slopes of our skin create arid expanses of inhospitable desert but the crevices and gorges that etch its surface provide shelter for many forms of life. Below the skin surface is an even richer world. Only the true specialist can survive here but those that do live a cosseted life protected from harsh extremes of temperature and bathed in a continuous supply of welcome nutrients.

For the most part we are blissfully unaware of the living cargo we carry. The only animals that usually make their presence felt are those that come to us for food.

SKIN DINING

MANY OF OUR UNINVITED guests are attracted by the oily up-wellings that moisten the landscape of our skin. These secretions are created by sweat glands exuding a nutritious soup of over a dozen amino acids, amply spiced with minerals and vitamins such as potassium, sodium, zinc, vitamin C and riboflavin.

In South-east Asia and South America colourful butterflies alight on the skin surface and delicately sip these secretions. Invariably, these visitors are males, attracted by the sodium salts they need to complete their sexual development. In tropical rainforests there are bees that specialise in feeding on these nourishing fluids. Fortunately stingless, thousands of these sweat bees may descend on a perspiring human.

Equally unwelcome are visiting flies. Musca sorbens, a close relative of the housefly, has made a speciality of feeding from the skin surface. Its proboscis, a mouth like a suction cap, is used to hoover up not only perspiration but also the fluids that moisten the surface of the eye. These annoying insects can effortlessly avoid the brush of a hand and immediately resettle to feed once the swipe has past. Their evasive skills are derived from lightning reflexes and a visual system that processes information 10 times more quickly than our own.

Our eye or skin surface usually offers a rock-like barrier to the probings of these flies, but when wounds create oozing caverns on the surface they descend in droves. Up to fifty at a time may feast on the nutrients that have been unearthed. With such a rich seam of food lying just beneath the skin it was inevitable that some flies found ways of excavating their own cavities.

THE EXCAVATORS

THE MOST ABUNDANT BITING flies are blackflies: varieties are found in almost every part of the world. The female needs a blood meal before she can lay her eggs and she relies on vision to find a suitable victim. The fly's mouth parts are an array of specialised cutting tools, which not only stretch the skin taut but at the same time saw through the surface, excavating crude cavities that well up with blood. A feeding fly may more than double its weight before it finishes its meal.

Mosquitoes have a far subtler method of extracting their food. They tap into the nutrient-rich veins below the surface using a fine proboscis made from two hypodermic tubes. Once inserted into a capillary, anticoagulant saliva is poured down a groove in one of the tubes to ensure that the blood runs free.

These blood-feeders hardly have an easy life. Their food supply is mobile and unpredictable and they have to rely on acute senses to find their meal.

Opposite above: In Papua New Guinea a butterfly shows its taste for the salts found in perspiration. Below: Sweat bees specialise in feeding on these nourishing fluids and are attracted to a sweat-drenched belt.

*The mosquito finds its human victim by following the carbon
dioxide trail created by our breath. Its proboscis taps the
nutrient-rich capillaries below the skin surface.*

Fortunately for them, we send out chemical signals to guide them every time
we take a breath as they respond to an increase in carbon dioxide in the air.
The heat gradient that surrounds our body sends out another cue, as do the
chemical components found in human sweat. Unable to avoid emitting these
tell-tale signs, in the tropics many people resort to mosquito nets in order to
prevent attack.

However, nets serve no protection against the attentions of sandflies.
These tiny midge-like insects, known as 'no-see-um' flies because of their
small size, can effortlessly slip through the mesh. They are a common nuisance
in tropical regions and frequently infiltrate buildings to feed on people and
their domestic animals.

Only one mammal has discovered the blood-feeding way of life and this
creature uses truly formidable senses to track people down.

THE VAMPIRE

EACH NIGHT, ACROSS CENTRAL and South America, vampire bats leave their caves to search for a blood meal. They are guided by the same ultrasonic echo-guidance system employed by most bats, but the prey they seek is far larger. Their sonic-imagers are tuned in to any mammal or bird.

As they descend they switch over to yet another sophisticated sense. The vampire's face is decorated by a convoluted patch of skin, a nose-leaf that is insulated from the bat's own body heat but responds to the blood heat of other animals. It uses this sense to home into blood-filled tissues, then its razor-sharp teeth ensure that the bite is painless. The vampire does not suck blood – instead, it laps the flowing liquid like a cat taking milk.

These bats attack any vertebrates and, although domesticated animals are the most common victims, they readily feed from humans. Although their bite is relatively innocuous, a small percentage of them carry rabies and this is where they pose a danger.

The vampire needs an array of refined senses to pinpoint its highly mobile food. Other less sophisticated bloodsuckers have found equally effect-ive methods of finding their victims.

BLOODSUCKERS

BLOOD-FEEDERS THAT LIVE IN water, such as the leech, rely on the ripples created by the movements of other creatures. It uses undulations of its body to swim unerringly towards the source of the disturbance. Once its sucker has made contact, it will feed until its body has expanded to nine times its original size.

Land leeches, found in the moist tropical forests of Asia and Africa, show similar voracious behaviour. Although an apparently simple animal with only rudimentary eyes, the leech can sense the arrival of humans and loops its body unerringly towards them. Just what stimulates the leech is uncertain. Like other blood-feeders, the carbon dioxide in our breath and the warmth of our bodies may provide telling signals. It may also respond to vibration. But the way that leeches can cross great distances to home in on a motionless person still appears almost miraculous.

Although the land leech has sophisticated and mysterious senses, it depends totally on the chance movements of animals for its meals. Sometimes, it may have to wait many months for a creature to pass into range. Even greater feats of patience are shown by the group of bloodsuckers known as ticks.

SITTING IT OUT

AN ADULT TICK CAN go seven years between meals. It bides its time, becoming totally immobile, but in damp weather it climbs a grass stem or twig in the hope that a mammal or bird will wander by. In parts of North America, among populations of snowshoe hare and grouse, the number of ticks waiting for their lucky break can reach over 2.8 million per square mile.

Even with time on the side of the tick, the odds are stacked against it, and in the unlikely event of an animal brushing past, it makes sure not to lose the opportunity. When its moment finally arrives, rows of backward-pointing teeth act as grappling irons to secure the tick to its host. Anchored firmly, the female may feast for nine days until her body is a bloated sphere.

In the desert regions of southern Africa a tick known as the sand tampan has found an ingenious way of cutting down the waiting time. It buries itself in the sand under the shade of a tree. Here, shrivelled and immobile, it can lurk for many months until an animal chooses its tree as a sunshade. As soon as it feels the vibrations and detects carbon dioxide percolating through the sand, the apparently lifeless tampan resurrects itself. Seconds later it emerges from the sand and crawls towards its victim. Several hundred tampans may descend on an unsuspecting human simultaneously.

By capitalising on the need of animals to seek shade the sand tampan has improved its chances of finding food. With luck dominating the lives of many blood-feeders, it was inevitable that some discovered ways of shortening the odds even more in their favour.

FLEA BITTEN

FORTUNATELY FOR BLOOD-FEEDERS, many of their hosts, including humans, create nests which they use for sleep or rest and which they inevitably share with other creatures. A blood-feeder that lays its eggs in the nest-lining guarantees that its offspring will meet the host.

This method of strategic targeting is relied on by the human flea and as a result each adult needs to lay only a few hundred eggs. Its young larvae thrive among the nest fibres, nourished by the confetti of skin and scurf that drifts down on them from their host.

The human flea must have been one of the first insects to take to a life in human nests and until recently its larvae commonly dwelt in the carpets and furnishings that make up the nest-lining of modern homes. Its pupae can survive almost indefinitely, so even if a room has been left vacant for years the fleas may still be there. The adults emerge as soon as they detect the vibrations made by returning footsteps.

*The sand tampan may wait for months buried under the shade
of a tree until a victim approaches. When one does, the tampan
quickly engorges itself with blood.*

The adult flea is designed for leaping. Its back legs are powered by a spring, made of the protein resilin, which is first cocked by powerful muscles. An increase in carbon dioxide signals that the host is near and the spring is released. This catapults the flea upwards. Its acceleration approaches twenty times that of a launching space shuttle. In the first five-hundredth of a second it will be travelling at 100 metres per second but it rapidly decelerates as it approaches its maximum altitude of around 20 centimetres. This is 120 times its own height and equivalent to a man jumping a quarter of a mile.

As the flea tumbles in space, its front legs are hooked out ready to grasp any hair. On landing, its sensitive mouth parts begin to explore the skin surface. Two lance-like blades, equipped with four rows of teeth, stab the skin and, like the mosquito, inject anticoagulant saliva to free the blood flow.

Once a a female has finished her meal she drops to the ground to lay her eggs. Usually she arrives back in the nest and so the eggs are laid in a prime location. Unfortunately for the human flea, the condition of human nests has undergone a decline. Central heating creates a climate that is far too arid and the vacuum cleaner sucks up the few eggs and larvae that survive. As a result, in Northern Europe the human flea is now more common in the nests of badgers, foxes and pigs, which are alternative hosts.

Cat fleas have fared far better as they actually prefer the drier atmosphere of modern homes. They even manage to escape the vacuum cleaner by thriving in the inaccessible strip between the carpet and the wall. Although the adult fleas prefer the blood of cats, they will readily bite us too, although they cannot yet survive solely on people. Several human blood-feeders started out by feeding on other animals that once shared our homes. The bedbug is believed to have begun its life with us in this way.

SNUG AS A BUG

BEDBUGS ORIGINATED IN THE Middle East, where they inhabited the caves of bats. At night the bugs would wait in crevices and, on the bats' return, they ventured out to feed on them. When humans moved into the cave the bugs happily took their blood instead. Then, when the people left, the bedbugs went with them. For most of history they were confined to the region they initially inhabited but, 1000 years ago, they began to benefit from increasing trade and, 500 years ago, they finally reached northern Europe. In the tropics a second species showed a similar increase, moving from South-east Asia to Africa and eventually to America.

In human homes the adult bugs spend the day hidden in cracks in walls and furniture or in the seams of mattresses. They can wait for over a year for a meal. Their activity is timed to the sleeping cycle of humans and in the dark hours of early morning they scurry across the bed sheets to search for their host. An unfed bug is wafer-thin but after five to ten minutes of feeding its body become distended and elongated with blood. Bedbugs find it difficult to survive in clean modern homes, but just 50 years ago they could be found in one house in ten in many British cities.

In tropical Africa people, while asleep, can fall prey to the Congo floor maggot. The adult maggot fly lays her eggs on the earth floor of huts, her young survive in cracks in the ground and they emerge at night to feed off the unwary. For the maggot this source of nourishment is far from secure, however, as it can be thwarted by the use of a raised platform for sleeping.

The cat flea has adapted to a life in human nests. Unlike the human flea it appreciates the dry atmosphere of modern homes.

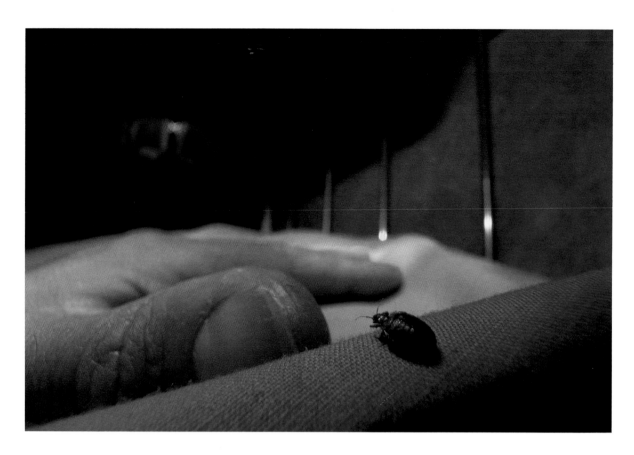

Bedbugs were originally cave-dwellers that fed from bats. They now time their blood-sucking activity according to the sleep cycle of humans.

Blood-feeders that have taken to lodging in human nests may have increased their chances of obtaining a blood meal but they still face a hazardous existence. One way of reducing the risk is for them to live at least part of their life on or inside our body.

UNDER OUR SKIN

THE COMMONEST ANIMALS THAT have taken to a subterranean life are the larvae of flies. It is easy to see how the habit developed. Flies that feed on wounds or sores sometimes lay their eggs there just as they do when feeding on carrion. Even the maggot of a housefly will flourish in a neglected wound although it will never consume living flesh. (In the past such fly maggots have even been used to clean out septic wounds.) Some species of flies turned their attention to healthy tissue and found a whole new world under our skin.

In the warmer regions of North and South America, one of these invaders is the screw-worm. The fly lays her eggs on the surface of the skin and, when the maggots emerge, they cooperate in excavating a cavity in which they will live until they are ready to pupate. Africa has its own version of the screw-worm and it also has the tumbu fly. The tumbu lays its eggs on the ground and its young find their way into their host by burrowing through the sole of the foot.

When finding a human nursery for its young the human bot-fly of South America leaves little to chance. It relies on the superior senses of a mosquito to do the searching. It glues about a dozen eggs to the bloodsucker's abdomen with quick-drying cement. A few days later, when the mosquito lands on a human to feed, the larvae detect the body warmth, burst out of their eggs and drop onto the skin below. The larvae develop in cysts just below the skin surface and emerge about two months later.

Even with a mosquito as a baby-carrier, the bot-fly cannot guarantee that its eggs always reach their target. Like other animals that rely on using humans to raise their young, locating us is the most unpredictable part of their life cycle. Some organisms avoid these risks altogether by spending their whole existence on our bodies.

These creatures are the true specialists. Perfectly adapted to this unique environment, they have given up the chance of living on any alternative host. Having made this commitment, their ultimate success or failure depends totally on our fortunes. The organisms that opted for a life with prehistoric humans ultimately hit the jackpot, for their numbers expanded along with ours and they can now be found across the globe.

FEELING LOUSY

THE LOUSE WAS ONE OF the most successful of these invaders. When it first took to inhabiting our bodies the human skin surface presented a very different landscape from what it does today. Like the other great apes, early humans were totally covered in a forest of hair.

When gorillas groom each other they attack the populations of lice that still flourish in their thick hair. These gorilla lice are slow-moving crab-like creatures with giant claws on their second and third pairs of legs. They use these claws to swing from hair to hair. A very similar type of louse still survives on some human bodies but it is confined to the regions that retain this ape-like hair. Even today human pubic lice (known as 'crabs') and gorilla lice are so similar they are difficult to tell apart. They are believed to have evolved from a form that lived on some ancestral ape.

As humans developed into the modern and relatively hairless homo sapiens, the deforestation separated two distinct populations of lice. The

Above: The head louse is one of our most successful companions.
It is actually on the increase in many cities.
Opposite: Among Bushmen, as in other tribal cultures, delousing
sessions are part of normal social life.

original form became trapped in the pubic regions, while another type got stranded in the thicket of hair left on top of the head. These two environments, separated by a vast expanse of desert-like skin, were habitats as contrasting and isolated as tropical and temperate forests.

The hair of the tropical zone was coarse, widely spaced and closest to that of early humans. Survival here depended on a good grip and a tendency not to wander. The slow-moving pubic louse was already adapted to this humid jungle. The hair of the temperate zone was thinner, densely packed and extended over a larger area. Here a more mobile form of louse developed. It had small claws on all three pairs of legs and its body was streamlined rather than crab-shaped, which allowed it to clamber swiftly though the dense forest.

Both types of lice lead similar lives. Each day the females produce eight

to ten eggs, which are glued to the base of the hair. Eight days later the young nymphs literally explode into the world. A nymph achieves this spectacular entrance by piercing the lid of the egg with its proboscis and sucking in air. The air pressure builds until finally the lid blasts off and the nymph is ejected. The nymph feeds on blood and will moult several times before it emerges as an adult louse. For the head louse the process takes about three months, but the pubic louse, cosseted in a warmer environment, takes only two weeks to reach maturity.

For many thousands of years the two species were confined to their own distinct forest regions. These acted as nature reserves against the deforestation that had occurred over the rest of the human body. But, as people began to wear clothes, a new ecological niche suddenly became available. The sedentary pubic louse was too specialised to exploit the fresh opportunities, but the more mobile and versatile head louse was quick to colonise. A new larger and hardier form developed that was able to live totally on the clothes. It clung to the fibrous tendrils of the cloth, only reaching onto the body to feed. It even laid its eggs on seams of garments, although it still relied on body warmth to help with incubation.

The body louse was able to recolonise a comparatively vast area of the human body, but its new life was not without risk. If clothes were removed the lice were literally left out in the cold, so the body louse adapted by becoming more resistant to temperature changes and starvation. It also laid many more eggs. A single female can produce 250 eggs, theoretically, in just eighty days, which could give rise to a colony of 5000 females. Such prodigious reproductive rates compensate for the riskier lives these settlers lead.

In recent years, cleanliness and the habit of removing underclothes at night has decimated populations of body lice, but pubic lice, transmitted through sexual encounters, still manage to survive. Head lice, which thrive even in clean hair, are actually increasing. They tend to infect schoolchildren and seem to prefer girls. Girls tend to have closer physical contact with each other and this helps the adult lice invade a new head of hair.

As well as being subjected to changes in the lifestyle of their host, lice have always been vulnerable to attack by grooming. The louse is well-protected against these assaults. Its cuticle can resist a pressure of one and a half kilograms, one million times its own weight. Many tribal people crush the lice with their teeth, and these delousing sessions are frequently a communal event. As the lice range in size from two to four millimetres they are quite visible to the human eye.

Smaller organisms are not so easily detected. A distant relative of the spider, known as the follicle mite, has become miniaturised beyond the capacity of human vision.

FOLLICLE FOLLIES

FOLLICLE MITES ARE TRANSPARENT worm-like scavengers less than three-tenths of a millimetre long. They spend most of their lives head down in a hair follicle, gripping the base of a hair with stumpy legs. Reaching their highest populations in areas rich in sebaceous glands, they are common around the chin, nose, forehead and nipples. Their favourite site appears to be the eyelids, where they live at the base of the eyelash hairs.

They mate with their heads still buried in a hair follicle and seek out a sebaceous gland to use as an egg chamber. The young develop in the follicle and emerge after three days, while their host is asleep. After exploring the skin surface for up to 36 hours they finally disappear down a new hair follicle and two and a half days later moult into adult mites. They seem to dislike modern soaps but thrive on skin creams and eye make-up. Follicle mites are totally harmless, which is just as well as they live unmolested on almost all human beings.

MINING MITE

MANY PEOPLE ARE ALSO home to a less benign organism known as scabies. Shaped somewhat like a hairy tortoise, this tiny mite constructs its own burrow by tunnelling through the surface of the skin. It prefers the more desolate hairless areas that other skin-dwellers usually avoid, liking the skin of the wrists, fingers, elbows and ankles as well as the soles of the feet and the palms of the hands.

The scabies mite's front two pairs of legs are equipped with suckers and a fine cutting edge, forming a sophisticated mining tool which they use in combination with razor-sharp jaws. With this equipment the mite tunnels into the skin at a rate of 2 millimetres each day, while backward-facing spines on its body help it grip the burrow walls. The male enters the female's burrow to mate, and she then lays up to 25 oval eggs at the rate of two or three per day. The young nymphs moult several times before they emerge as adults.

Unlike the unobtrusive follicle mites, an infestation of scabies is usually noticed, as the burrows can cause severe itching. Numbers are usually kept down by scratching, although sometimes an immunity to their presence develops and this can cause a population explosion. Over two million mites have been found on one individual.

The size of the smallest speck of dust, scabies mites themselves can only just be seen by human eyes. Although tiny, they are however lumbering giants compared with the majority of organisms that inhabit the skin surface. As the mite crawls across the epidermal cells, which appear like large flattened cobblestones, it continually kicks and trips over myriads of far smaller organisms. These are our skin bacteria.

BUSTLING BACTERIA

THE MAJORITY OF BACTERIA ON the skin surface are relatively static sphere or rod shapes, but others propel themselves around with rapidly vibrating tails in a frenzy of activity. About once every 20 minutes each bacterium constricts itself around the middle and divides in two. Each half is a living replica of the other, which in turn is capable of dividing again.

Although the population can therefore theoretically double every 20 minutes a population crisis never occurs because of the fragmentary nature of the skin surface. Epidermal cells continually flake away from the body. As they float into the air they carry bacteria with them. Around 10 million skin cells and their cargo of bacteria are cast adrift by every human being each day. Every minute 25 000 bacteria float off into space, cancelling out those materialising by division.

The skin bacteria not only have to cope with an unstable living surface but they have to tolerate a salty or acid environment and for much of the time hostile desert-like conditions. Only a few vigorous bacteria survive on this inhospitable terrain, but those that do flourish often appear in astronomical numbers.

The most favoured localities are the forehead, where 800 000 bacteria cram onto an area the size of a postage stamp, and the scalp, where an incredible six million jostle together over the same area. The back is relatively inhospitable and the postage stamp sized population there drops to a mere 200 000. As few as 45 000 survive over the same space on the fore-arm.

Although skin shedding keeps down the surface population, it has little effect on the majority of skin bacteria. Most spend their lives protected in the crevices, pits and glands that fracture the skin surface. In areas rich in sebaceous glands, ten times as many of these deep-dwelling species survive than on the surface. Secure in the nooks and crannies, the inhabitants have to regulate their own populations.

Numbers tend to stabilise at a level that the available nutrients can support. Once this has been reached other bacteria then find it difficult to invade. This arrangement is fortunate for humans as our bodies are continually exposed to potentially harmful organisms which our indigenous bacteria usually manage to keep at bay.

INFECTING INVADERS

THE AIR IS LITERALLY teeming with bacteria. Many ride the skin particles that are the main component of house dust. Wafted on the air currents of our breath, each hour between 1500 and 14 000 of these micro-organisms invade our nose and mouth.

The nasal passages are relatively hostile and few bacteria manage to survive here. Those that reach the mouth fare little better as many are engulfed in unwelcoming saliva. A few specialists do find a home and these may breed in considerable numbers. Life is hazardous for these colonisers. Each mealtime their population experiences a catastrophic collapse as they are overwhelmed by torrents of food and saliva, but the bacteria propagate quickly and within a few hours they have compensated for the losses.

The mouth bacteria's most productive period is while their host is asleep

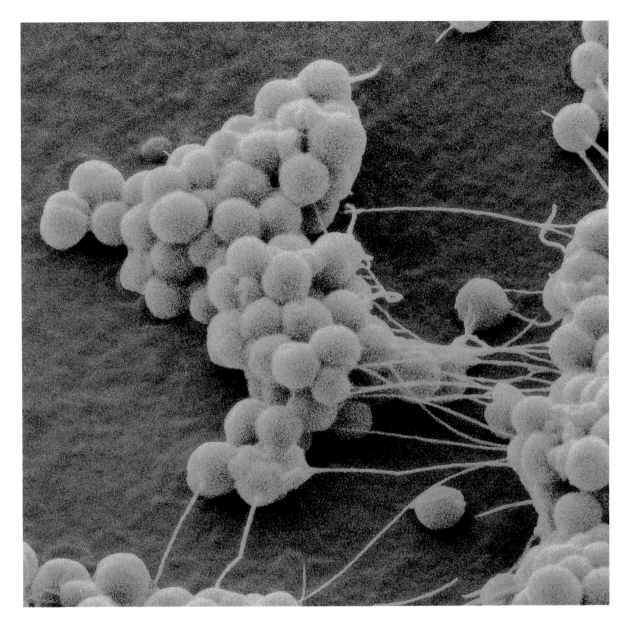

*Staphylococci bacteria are common inhabitants of the skin. Every
20 minutes they divide, compensating for the half million that
are cast adrift on shed skin flakes every hour.*

and by the morning their population is at its peak. Their respite is only temporary, though, as a vigorous scrub with a toothbrush will slash numbers by 80 per cent. The 20 per cent that remain soon redress the balance.

Few bacteria survive in the stomach but the lower intestine and caecum are bacterial havens and these organisms make up about half of the dry weight of faeces.

Much of the interior of the body is actually bacteriologically sterile and if bacteria manage to invade these regions they often cause disease. Staphylococci bacteria, which are common and quite harmless on the skin, can cause poisoning, sometimes fatal, if they enter the blood system.

The inside of the womb is also free of bacteria and, if a baby is to survive in the outside world, it must acquire its population of bacteria quickly at birth. This begins to happen immediately it enters the vaginal canal and at the moment of birth the mother's anal area donates more bacteria. Even in the most sterilised hospitals the birth attendants unwittingly contribute strains of their own personal bacteria.

This infection is not only unavoidable, it is vital. Within a few hours a population of bacteria is established in the baby's mouth and after 13–18 hours the nose and throat are infected too. The bacterial population of the skin similarly increases, Within 24 hours of birth numbers in the armpit have reached 6000 per square centimetre and nine days later they have begun to stabilise at around 80 000 over the same area.

At about this age its been shown that mothers can recognise their own babies by smell alone. This is no coincidence. As the bacteria break down skin secretions, they create ammonia by-products that are a major component of body odour.

PERSONAL PERFUME

THESE ODOURS ARE SO important to many mammals that glands on their bodies empty into special pockets and pouches which act as breeding grounds for the smell-producing bacteria. Humans are no exception: our apocrine glands are concentrated in the armpit and groin areas. They secrete into the only parts of the body, apart from the head, still covered in hair. The hairs not only provide a protective forest for the bacteria but they also create a large evaporative surface which helps propagate the smell.

The bacteria help establish a personal odour that is as unique as a fingerprint. It is this characteristic smell that guides a tracker dog along a human trail, and even the far less sensitive nose of a human can identify these individual odours if given a chance. Recently it has become fashionable to eradicate body odours entirely and chemical warfare is being waged on the micro-organisms that the hairy parts of the body are designed to protect.

The deodorants that we apply to the main bacterial breeding grounds contain aluminium compounds that block the secreting pores, as well as strong bactericides. Within 30 minutes of a deodorant attack the majority of the resident bacteria will be dead, a few resilient individuals will struggle on for up to two hours and some will continue to cling to life protected in the base of the hairs or attached to clothes.

The process of recolonisation begins with these few survivors but, with the majority of the indigenous population wiped out, there is nothing to prevent less desirable bacteria invading as well. With the original balance destroyed these marauding micro-organisms can create havoc.

The dangers of upsetting the natural balance of these skin-dwellers became apparent when vaginal deodorants were first marketed. When the resident bacteria were wiped out they left behind a vacant ecological niche that was invaded by bacteria normally found in the intestine. As these multiplied they irritated the skin surface and created conditions that allowed the invasion of microscopic fungi such as those that cause thrush. Once these ecological disaster zones had been created they never quite recovered. Consequently vaginal deodorants were removed from sale.

The microscopic fungi that flooded in were single-celled organisms known as yeasts. Only a few species can survive on the dry surface of the skin but, like bacteria, they may reach phenomenal numbers. On the surface of the scalp and nose they reach a density of half a million over every square centimetre. They are oval in shape and about twice as large as the average bacterium.

A breakdown in the body's equilibrium can also cause these skin fungi to become invasive. Athlete's foot is caused by a fungus that is present on most individuals. After a broad-based antibiotic has wrought havoc on the indigenous population of bacteria the fungus often undergoes a population explosion to fill the biological vacuum.

The ecology of the human body is as subtly complex as that of any terrestrial landscape. Symptoms of disease appear when the natural balance has been upset.

VIRAL SPIRAL

HUMAN DISEASE CAN ALSO be caused by viruses. A virus can hardly be considered as an organism. It consists of just a few strands of the genetic coding substances, DNA and RNA, covered by a protein coat.

This tiny bundle of chemicals cannot survive alone. It needs the succour provided by living cells. Once inside, it plunders the cell's contents in order to create hundreds of living replicas of itself. These clones then leave to invade new cells. We feel the effects of this viral looting when we suffer from colds, 'flu, measles or mumps.

PREDATORS AND GRAZERS

ANY BALANCED ECOSYSTEM INCORPORATES predators and grazers and the human body is no exception. On this miniature scale these roles are taken by protozoa. These single-celled animals are comparative giants, up to 10 times larger than the bacteria many of them feed on. They dry out and die on the parched skin surface but multiply wherever there is a permanent film of moisture.

Two main groups are involved: amorphous amoeba that use their fluid bodies to engulf food, and oval or pear-shaped flagellates that swim around by vibrating a whip-like hair. Both types live in the mouth. They survive in the spaces between the teeth, living off food particles and bacteria. In this hazardous home they are in constant danger of being crushed or swallowed. Few generally manage to survive but whenever there is a bacterial infection they graze the flourishing crop and experience a population boom.

Different protozoa are found in the intestine. The commonest is Entamoeba coli: half the world's human population has this intestinal companion. Like most protozoa it is totally harmless and lives on minute particles of food and bacteria. A related species, Entamoeba histolytica, sometimes produces an enzyme which digests the cells of the gut wall. The ulcerating cavities that result cause symptoms of amoebic dysentery. It is not in an organism's interest to destroy its living environment so usually this entamoeba avoids this destructive action and lives harmoniously with its host.

Organisms that have had a long-standing relationship with their host tend to be the least destructive – the most successful are not even noticed.

In recent years a gut flagellate known as Giardia has become common in industrial societies: an infection with this can cause nausea, cramps and diarrhoea. For the majority of people a Giardia infection is unpleasant or even dangerous but a considerable number show no symptoms at all. It seems that in these people's bodies a more benign stage of the relationship with the organism is beginning to develop.

BITTEN BY THE BUG

SOME OF THE PROTOZOA that cause human disease have established a balanced relationship with other mammals. Flagellates known as trypanosomes have taken to a life in the blood of African game animals. Many of their hosts show no symptoms at all.

They use tsetse flies to transport themselves from host to host. The tsetses find their blood meal, sometimes from as much as 30 kilometres away, by following the smell of the animal's breath upwind. When the fly bites, the

*The tsetse fly homes in on the breath of game animals and cattle.
If it bites a human being it may inject the protozoa that cause
sleeping sickness.*

trypanosomes are sucked up and they begin to multiply in the fly's gut. Two weeks later they migrate to the salivary glands and are dribbled out when the tsetse bites again. Although tsetses are attracted to the smell of game animals the final approach relies on vision. The coarse fragmentary view presented by their compound eye is easily confused by any dark moving shape. In this way, a biting tsetse may transfer the trypanosomes to people.

Poured into the subterranean tunnels of the human bloodstream, the trypanosomes have entered a canal system which has branches leading to every part of the body. Sometimes they find themselves in the backwater of a capillary, sometimes they cascade through the cataracts of the heart. They may take refuge in the quieter waters of the lymph gland but, wherever they are, they multiply. After two weeks they finish their vascular wanderings and migrate en masse into the nervous system. Their host now notices their presence through the lethargic symptoms of sleeping sickness.

Humans have no natural resistance to this invasion and neither do their domesticated animals. Trypanosomes have evolved to live happily in the

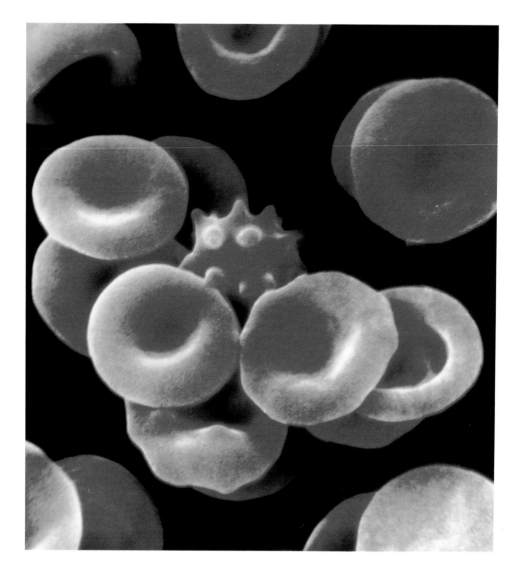

Red blood corpuscles are used as a temporary home by the
plasmodia that cause malaria.

bodies of the indigenous game animals, not inside these newer arrivals.

It is for the same reason that humans have problems with malaria. This protozoa's preferred hosts are wild animals and when they find themselves in people they can cause fatal consequences. In some parts of Africa, where humans have been exposed to the local malaria for many years, a limited tolerance develops.

Malaria is carried by mosquitoes and the offending organisms, plasmodia, are injected into the blood as they bite. Within half an hour this waterway has carried them to their destination. They disembark in the liver and begin to invade its cells. They then split in two and invade more cells. A few days later they set sail back in the blood vessels. Like giant lifebuoys, doughnut-shaped blood corpuscles float alongside them. The plasmodia move on board, begin to split again and periodically cast themselves adrift to search for new blood cells. Each time this happens, toxins are produced and these create the cyclical symptoms of malaria. Eventually the splitting creates male and female sexual forms and these stay adrift in the blood until they are sucked up by a mosquito.

They reproduce inside the mosquito's gut and eventually invade the salivary gland: up to 200 000 may be crammed into this tiny gland waiting to invade a new host. A mosquito is so effective both as an incubator and as a way of seeking out and infecting people that many other organisms that live in human bodies rely on it for help.

WORMS THAT TURN

THE FILARIAL WORM TIMES its trips into the bloodstream to coincide with the activity of mosquitoes. The adults, as thin as sewing thread but as long as a finger, live coiled up in the lymph glands. Occasionally they cause blockages, which result in the gross swellings known as elephantiasis. Their microscopic larvae live in the lymph glands too, but between 10 p.m. and 4 a.m. they migrate into the bloodstream to keep their appointment with their insect host.

The larva of the African eye-worm also shows clockwork precision in its trips into the bloodstream, but it is carried by day-active mangrove flies and so synchronises its vascular journeys to the daylight hours. The adult worm lives in the layer of connective tissue found beneath the skin and generally is only noticed when its wanderings take it across the eye.

Both the filarial worm and the eye-worm are nematodes, relatives of the earthworms found in gardens. Some nematodes continue an underground existence in the depths of the alimentary canal.

Threadworms are so successful that in North America and Europe they are the most frequently found form of infection after the common cold. These small, whitish worms live in the intestine and appendix. Although relatively harmless, they have the disconcerting habit of leaving the body at night to lay their eggs around the anus and then returning inside. The eggs cause an irritation and, when the host scratches, they are picked up on the fingernails and later transferred to the mouth.

Sometimes the egg-laying adults get lost. These shrivel up and then explode, releasing hundreds of eggs. These are so light they float on the air and sometimes settle on food. In this way they find themselves inside a new host. For those worms that shed their eggs directly on the ground dispersal is equally hazardous.

EGGS EXTRAORDINAIRE

TO ENSURE SOME OF their offspring survive, many nematode worms compensate by laying prodigious quantities of eggs. Each day the intestinal hookworm releases 10 000 to 20 000 eggs, which reach the ground in human faeces. It has to lay so many because the young larvae need to be trodden on if they are to find a new host. They seek out the highest points on the ground and wait for a foot to appear. They then burrow through the skin and invade the blood. Enough survive this chancey stage to maintain high rates of infection. In parts of India 80 per cent of the human population are infected, although few would be aware of any symptoms.

Ascaris is an even more prodigious egg-producer, each female laying 27 million eggs. They require so many because their life cycle is extremely hazardous. The adults live in the small intestine and the eggs leave the body in faeces. The eggs only survive in moist soil and have to be transferred to the mouth on food and fingers. The few that reach the human intestine then have a perilous and apparently pointless journey ahead of them.

The larvae hatch, penetrate the gut wall and enter a blood vessel. Going with the flow, they meander around the body until they reach the liver. Here they stay for a few days and then return to the bloodstream. Flushed into capillaries in the lungs they transfer to an air passage and travel up the trachea. Finally they arrive at the back of the throat. This is a tricky moment. If their host coughs now they will be propelled into space and the journey will end in disaster. If their luck stays with them, their host suppresses the tickling sensation and they are swallowed. They end up back in the intestine where their journey began. This time, their restlessness over, they settle to grow into adult roundworms.

Why these creatures should make this seemingly senseless journey is a mystery, but they may be following behaviour patterns left over from a time when the roundworm had a second host in its life cycle.

Humans also play host to a nematode known as trichinella. From the worm's point of view this relationship is a disaster. The worms produce live young which, instead of leaving the body, encyst themselves in their host's muscle. Here they wait for their host to be eaten. Unfortunately for trichinella, we have become expert at avoiding this fate, so those that infect human bodies are doomed to die with their hosts.

The high trichinella infection rates found in people in industrialised nations are maintained through eating infected pigs. The practice of including scraps of pork in pig swill ensures enough pigs continue to be infected to compensate for the nematodes hitting a dead end inside a human body.

Because of the long association between pigs and humans we tend to share many of the same animal invaders. We have become an important home to the adult stage of the pork tapeworm.

GOING TO GREAT LENGTHS

TAPEWORMS LIVE IN THE intestines and are perfectly adapted to this specialised existence. To counteract the continual peristaltic waves that threaten to dislodge them, their head consists of suckers and two circular rows of hooks that grip the gut wall. Behind the head, rows of body segments known as proglottides extend for up to 5 metres. Tapeworms have no intestine – instead, they absorb food directly from the liquids that flow over them. Their outer surface is effectively their stomach lining and it is immune to the digestive juices of their host. With its gut on the outside, the tapeworm is free to devote its inside to reproduction.

Each proglottis contains both male and female sexual organs. These can fertilise each other or other segments. On the rare occasions that two tapeworms inhabit the same intestine they will mate together, often simultaneously over many segments. After mating, the organs degenerate and the proglottis becomes a uterus packed with over 100 000 eggs. Each tapeworm may consist of 1000 proglottides, all in different stages of development. The last proglottides contain the ripest eggs and 10 of them are shed each day. As might be expected from this phenomenal reproductive rate of a million eggs a day, the offspring face many hazards before they find their way back to the human body. They first have to be eaten by another host, which is most commonly a pig. Humans are reinfected when the pig is eaten and the cysts lodged in the muscle are swallowed.

When people discovered fire they must have increased the odds against tapeworms reaching the adult stage as the cysts are killed by the heat of cooking. In many countries the pork tapeworm is now rare or extinct but the beef tapeworm, which can reach the astonishing length of 27 metres, is still thriving due to the habit of eating rare steaks. The eggs can survive the sewage process. If swallowed by gulls at sewage outlets or on settling beds, they may be carried to pastureland, where they are passed by the gull unharmed. The life cycle continues when grazing cows eat the eggs.

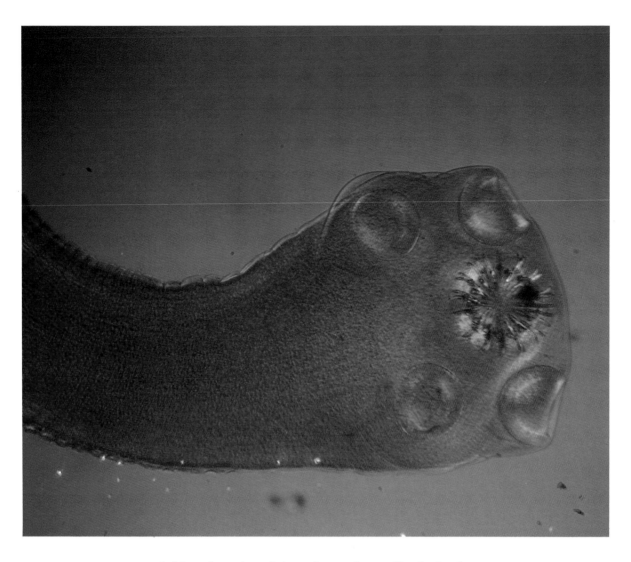

A false colour view of the suckers and grappling hooks that
allow a tapeworm to anchor itself to the gut wall.

Because of their size, tapeworms are perhaps the most spectacular of the animals that inhabit the human body, but they are so well adapted to their host that many people with one show no adverse symptoms.

OUR LIVING LEGACY

FEW PEOPLE WOULD WILLINGLY play host to a tapeworm, even if it caused little discomfort, but whether we like it or not we cannot avoid sharing our bodies with millions of other organisms.

Every human being carries a living cargo of these creatures. Countless millions of bacteria swarm over our skin surface and dwell in our intestines, while follicle mites shelter at the base of our hairs. Many people also offer sanctuary to some of the larger organisms such as lice or one of the many varieties of worms. Fortunately, the majority of these lodgers are perfectly adapted to a life on our bodies. They cause us little discomfort and some are even essential for our survival – though a number cause illness and some can even kill.

The incidence of disease started to increase when people were drawn together as they began to grow crops. The greater proximity allowed existing diseases, which were maintained at a low level under the original human living patterns, to be more readily transmitted. When towns developed, epidemics that could wipe out whole populations began to become common.

Although recent medical advances have had an impact on some of these harmful invaders, even causing the smallpox virus to become extinct, many diseases are still flourishing and some new ones are appearing. The growth of travel has exposed many formerly rare diseases to a human population with a lifestyle that presents a perfect opportunity for efficient dispersal. Many of these diseases once existed in balance with the local human populations and only became a problem when exposed to people with no natural immunity. Others lived in harmony with animal populations and only caused devastation once they leapt across the species gap onto humans – the AIDS virus is simply one example of many diseases that are believed to have begun in this way. In this case the original host is thought to have been a monkey.

Organisms that invade the human body and cause serious illness are actually ill-adapted to their host. They only thrive when we are suffering from conditions of overcrowding and stress and are relatively scarce compared with the organisms that live on our bodies without causing us damage. It is these harmless companions that are perhaps the true beneficiaries of our success.

To put things into perspective, a greater number of these benign organisms inhabit a single human body than there are people on earth. If we are unaware of our relationship to the creatures that are so close to us, what can we know of the life of the planet at large?

An elephant is rewarded for a day's work by being scrubbed and massaged. This helps reinforce the bond between elephant and mahout.

CHAPTER
6
LIFE IN THE
BALANCE

IN THE BUSHLANDS OF NORTHERN KENYA, a bird known as the greater honey-guide is an entomologist of some distinction. Its chosen subject is bees and each day it flies over this parched terrain of scrub and rocky crags to study their activity. It knows so much about its subject that every hive across an area of over 100 square miles has been discovered and memorised. These daily flights update the information and allow the honey-guide to record which hives are still active and which deserted.

It needs to collate this data because it survives by feeding on the wax and grubs of bees. But even with its extensive knowledge the bird still has difficulties procuring a meal. Most of the hives, protected deep in rock fissures and the boles of trees, are inaccessible. Its fine bill, designed for extracting grubs from the combs, is useless at breaking through to reach the nests. To overcome the problem it has evolved a relationship with people that is among the most remarkable on earth.

As soon as the honey-guide hears the sound of human voices it flies towards them. Perching in a nearby tree, it uses a persistent, dual-toned call to attract attention, and then, flitting restlessly from perch to perch, it waits for their response. If they show no interest, the bird soon flies off to search for others.

It seeks a particular type of person – a member of the Boran tribe, who specialise in collecting honey from wild hives. These honey-gatherers use haunting whistles to help the bird locate them. As soon as the honey-guide arrives they immediately move towards it. The bird responds by flying away, using a conspicuous undulating flight to signal that the people should follow.

In the dense scrub the honey-guide disappears from sight within seconds but it is never gone for long. Once the bird has reconfirmed the position of the nearest hive it flies back to find the gatherers. Checking again that the men are still following, it flies off once more in the direction of the hive. Throughout the trek the Boran maintain contact with the bird by whistling and talking to it, and the bird regularly returns to keep the people on course.

This toing and froing may continue for as much as 2 kilometres until the men are drawn close to the hive. The bird then perches nearby and signals the end of the honey-gatherers' quest by emitting a softer, less persistent call.

The honey-guide watches as the men prepare to break into the hive. The process may take some time, for the bees are dangerous. A stinging bee releases a chemical into the air that causes the others to descend in a persistent swarm so the gatherers use smoke to subdue the bees before they open up the colony. The bird waits patiently until the men have safely gathered the honey. They always leave behind a piece of comb containing grubs and as they depart the honey-guide swoops down to claim its reward.

Such a perfect partnership between people and a wild creature is unusual, but it is not unique. It could only develop among people whose lives are still entwined with the natural world. The story of human history has been one of increasing separation from other animals and, inevitably, as people left the hunting and gathering way of life behind, such close relationships became rarer. Those that remain are in danger of dying out. Nevertheless, today, in several parts of the world bottle-nosed dolphins continue a partnership with fishermen every bit as remarkable as that between the honey-guide and the Boran.

DIRECTED BY DOLPHINS

HUMANS AND DOLPHINS HAVE the most advanced brains of any of earth's organisms but they use them in very different ways. As the dolphin swims it is aware of the tiny variations in the earth's magnetic field created by the underlying rocks. It becomes familiar with the local magnetic distortions and creates a mental map of these features just as we develop a visual impression of our home town. Like the bat, the dolphin also gleans a detailed picture of its surroundings using sound instead of light waves. It emits ultrasound from a swelling, the melon, on its forehead and from the reflections, picked up through its jaw, it creates a sonar image. Even in the murkiest water it can find its way around.

Such sophisticated sensory powers require elaborate processing and much of the dolphin's brain is given over to analysing this kind of information. The human brain is no more sophisticated but it has developed in a fashion

In the bushlands of Northern Kenya, a greater honey-guide is familiar with all the bees' nests over an area of a hundred square miles. Boran honey-gatherers call to the bird to guide them to active hives.

that allows more reasoning power, although it would be hard pushed to cope with the complex sensory input routinely processed by the dolphin.

Two species with such a complementary combination of talents would be at an advantage if they cooperated in catching food. This is exactly what happens in several regions around the world.

The custom has developed in places as diverse as Australia, parts of the Mediterranean, South America and Mauritania. As the dolphins use their sonar to search for fish, the echoes from their high-pitched squeaks and whistles are sometimes interrupted by low-frequency thuds and the muffled sounds of human voices. These come from fishermen slapping the water and shouting to attract the dolphins' attention. The dolphins have learnt to associate these sounds with schools of fish appearing near the shore. As they swim towards the fishermen their sonar soon picks up the shoal. Their ultrasound penetrates the fishes' body tissue making even the skeletons detectable. The dolphins then begin herding their ghostly prey towards the fishermen. The fishes' escape is blocked by this human trap of spears or nets waiting at the shore. As the shoal swirls in confusion the dolphins plunge through the melee to take their share.

Both dolphins and fishermen benefit from the partnership and so the cooperative technique has developed separately in different parts of the world. It reaches perfection in the shallows lying off the town of Laguna, near the southern tip of Brazil.

In the frequently opaque water people have difficulty seeing the shoals of mullet that enter the shallows, but few pass undetected by the dolphin's sonar. When a shoal is discovered the dolphin actually signals its position to the fishermen. A sophisticated understanding has developed between the dolphins and their human accomplices and as they herd the fleeing fish before them they actually indicate, by a characteristic rolling dive, the exact moment the men should cast their nets. The dolphins' sole reward is the chance to catch mullet panicked by encircling mesh, but this is enough to maintain the partnership.

In Laguna the cooperative fishing began several hundred years ago. The young learn by watching their parents. In this way the techniques involved are handed down, in the families of both humans and dolphins, from one generation to the next.

In Bangladesh, fishermen employ a similar fishing technique using otters, but there is a significant difference: the otters are kept and bred in captivity and therefore have been coerced into the arrangement.

In Bangladesh, otters harnessed to boats are used to drive fish
into the fishermen's nets.

OTTER FISHERMEN

IN THE WILD, SMOOTH Indian otters often hunt in family groups and, to increase their catch, they spread out to drive the fish before them. Fishermen make use of the otter's herding ability to drive fish into their nets. A family of up to seven animals is kept by each fishermen and together they patrol the creeks and backwaters that intersect southern Bangladesh.

While travelling in the fishermen's low-slung skiffs these aquatic creatures peer out at the world through the bars of a wooden crate. Once they reach the fishing grounds a hatch is opened and they plunge into the water. Now in their natural element the otters' lithe shapes dip and dive through the water surface as they scan for fish and crabs.

Their bulbous eyes are adapted to focus under water but even they cannot deal with the haze of silt that clouds most of the river. Instead they rely on fine sensory whiskers to help detect the fishes' movements. Whatever they catch they keep. As the fish dart away the enveloping mesh of the fishermen blocks their escape. The net stretches along the length of the boat submerged by two poles positioned at each end. When it is full the fishermen raise the poles to decant their catch into the hull.

Harnesses keep the adult otters to either end of the boat and, although free to swim in a wide arc, they have learnt never to take fish from inside the nets. Their young swim free and as they master the art of catching food they swoop and plunge in synchrony with their parents.

Without the otters' help the fishermen would net only a fifth of their catch. The practice is so important to the fishermen and their dependents that in Bangladesh an estimated half million people rely on the otters for subsistence. In this, the most overpopulated country of the world, wild otters are now scarce but around 100 000 work alongside people. They readily breed in captivity so the practice ensures their survival here, but unlike dolphins they have been pressured into the partnership. In Asia, a similar kind of forced relationship is found between people and elephants.

ELEPHANT RIDES

FOR OVER 2500 YEARS, the Asian elephant has been used in war, in ceremonial roles and for manual work such as forestry. Until recently, most working elephants were taken from the wild as rearing them proved too time-consuming to be viable. To speed the process, elephants were formerly caught around the preferred age of ten years. The experience of capture, which has now been banned in India and Thailand, but still continues in Burma, was terrifying for the animals involved.

The working relationship between elephant and mahout may
last for 50 years.

Elephants are highly social animals. Their herds, consisting of females and their young as well as juvenile males, are led by a dominant female. When danger threatens, this matriarch stands and defends the herd or leads it to safety. At the sound of human voices her forehead resonates with a low rumbling sound, pitched below human hearing, to warn the herd to move.

When pursued by elephant-catchers a matriarch finds that, over several weeks, the encounters become more frequent. Initially, simply by moving her herd back into the forest she can avoid direct contact, but soon the confrontations become increasingly disturbing. Blazing fires may even block their paths. As the herd crashes back into the forest they encounter more people. They attempt to move away again, but once more a noisy wall of human beings blocks their retreat. As the elephants break for freedom they choose the line of least resistance. The escape route leads inexorably to an impenetrable forest of tree-trunks. As the elephants desperately seek a way through, a gate closes behind them. They are now trapped in a stockade.

After a few hours the gate opens and new elephants appear and begin to encircle them. On their backs, but unnoticed by the trapped animals, are

A logging elephant may learn 40 commands. The most important involve pressure applied to the back of the neck by the foot of the mahout.

the diminutive figures of humans. Unseen, one of the riders slips down and ties a rope around a distracted creature's leg. This tether, pulled by the tame elephants, forces the frightened captive from the stockade.

Other techniques for catching elephants, such as pitfall traps dug along elephant paths, and roping young animals away from the herd, were also used in the past. But whatever the method of capture the training follows similar lines. The elephant is securely tied by both front feet and starved for several days to make her weak and acquiescent. All this time she is accompanied by men who sing and talk to her to accustom her to human presence, while also preventing her from sleeping. Tame elephants show her how to take proffered food and then the real training begins.

One trainer stands at the front end and the other at the tail, and elephants to either side of her act as reassuring companions. If the elephant responds correctly to a human command she is rewarded with food, if she makes the wrong move she is prodded with a stick. Her only company is now the trained elephants that help subdue and control her and the humans that alternately act with kindness or harshness. As the elephant learns the correct responses she finds that life becomes easier and she begins to build up a relationship with the person who rewards her with titbits. Eventually, having learnt the main commands and accepted a human on her back, her working life gets under way.

A logging elephant may learn 40 verbal and physical commands. In India, the most important of these involve pressure applied to the back of the ear by the foot of the mahout that rides her. A forward push with both feet tells the elephant to move forward, a push with a single foot tells the elephant to turn and heels pushed in against the body instruct the elephant to reverse. Through these broad commands the elephant knows which way to go, but even the simplest movement of a log requires a sophisticated array of commands and responses as well as a high degree of intelligent interpretation by the elephant.

Throughout the 50 working years that an elephant may stay with the mahout the relationship develops into one of an almost intuitive under-standing. By scratching the elephant in a particular way behind the ear, the mahout can cause his charge to respond with infrasonic calls of pleasure. The forehead flutters and, from this sounding board, rumbles produced in the larynx and pitched below and at the lower limits of human hearing spread out across the forest. These sounds, only recently recognised by science, have been known by the mahouts for centuries. They can be heard by other elephants up to 7 kilometres away.

Although the elephant has been coerced into work, once the trauma of capture and training is over its life is far from arduous. The working day consists of two shifts of around two hours each. Once work is finished the elephants are taken to water and they now have an hour of unadulterated fun as they are scrubbed and massaged by the mahouts. This practice is more than simple hygiene as it helps reinforce the bond between the mahout and the elephant. It goes some way to replacing the social interactions that the elephant lost when taken captive.

Although close, the relationship depends on the mahout maintaining dominance, and he never allows his animal to disobey a command. But it is a fragile partnership. The elephant could kill the mahout with one swing of its muscular trunk. Mahouts who overstep the mark do not last for long.

In Thailand monkeys also work alongside people and there are similarities both in the training and the maintenance of the relationship.

Obeying commands from its trainer, a macaque can pick up to
800 coconuts a day. It is a relationship that depends on the
human maintaining the upper hand.

MONKEY BUSINESS

IN THE MAMMAL WORLD walking on two legs is an exclusively human activity, but not in southern Thailand. On the palm-fringed beaches of Ko Samui, a pig-tailed macaque, using this humanoid gait, approaches a coconut tree. Here the human similarity ends and, in a single bound, the monkey is on the trunk and sprinting upwards. Within seconds it has climbed the 60 foot palm and has reached the coconuts nestling in the crown. Its pace now changes. Each nut is carefully inspected until it finds one that is ripe. Using either hands or feet the macaque rotates the coconut until its stalk is severed and it plummets earthwards. The macaque continues until all the ripe coconuts have been removed, and only then does it return to the ground. The fallen coconuts are now retrieved and, walking again on two legs, it carries each one in its arms to a waiting basket. Throughout this remarkable display of coordination a human has been watching the animal and, when the monkey is unsure of what to do, guides it with encouraging commands.

The training of the macaque began when it was a baby. The first step involved simply learning to turn the coconut on a spindle held by the trainer. Each time it made the right move it received a reward of food and praise. By a process of repetition and reward it not only learnt how to remove coconuts but also which ones were diseased and, by their colour, which ones were ripe. After three to five months, it could climb the palms and carry out its tasks with only the minimum of guidance. Its great intelligence made it a ready and adaptable pupil. Although it had to learn the basic skills, when up the tree it has to make many of its own decisions. When fully trained a macaque can pick as many as 800 coconuts a day. Some of the most accomplished can even lay poison for rodent pests in the crown of the tree.

The relationship between the owner and the macaque is inevitably close and there is obvious affection between the two. But the human is always in control and the relationship depends on maintaining this dominance. The human-like gait is an affectation that the owner encourages to show the extent of his control, for the monkey is equally able to carry a coconut by holding the stalk in its teeth. Every so often the monkey will put the relationship to the test by refusing to perform a task but the owner will threaten or even smack the monkey to ensure that he does not lose his influence. This disciplining is little different from that experienced in the wild by monkeys challenging their position in the social hierarchy, but there is a crucial difference in the relationship. The monkey cannot escape from it.

Humans control almost every aspect of the lives of domesticated animals in a similar way. Sometimes this manipulation is directed solely towards providing entertainment.

PRIZE FIGHTERS

IN HAADYAI, SOUTHERN THAILAND, a bull, guided by a rope passed through his nose, passes a crowd of expectant human spectators. A gate opens and he enters the ring. As he sniffs the ground he picks up the scent of other bulls and begins to paw the ground. He has come here to fight. In his corner, ringside attendants begin to mop his enormous brow, giving particular attention to his horns. As a finishing touch his neck is smeared with banana, which ensures that it is slippery to the touch.

In the opposite corner, his rival is given similar attention and, when the bell sounds, the two are led towards each other. When the restraining ropes are released the pugilists are on their own. As they size each other up, they paw the ground again. Then, with heads lowered, they charge. The contest is a battle of strength. For minutes they push against each other, neither giving ground. Horning is an effective tactic so they frequently change the position of their heads to gain an advantage. But the ultimate aim is to push the rival away. Eventually, one gains the upper hand and, with a determined charge, carries his opponent backwards. This may be with so much force that the rival leaves the ground but usually he simply backs away and then runs.

The fight may not end here. The loser may decide to go for a second bout and may even go on to win. But usually the bull recognises defeat and immediately gives in. The bulls have fought many times and so the vanquished animal knows what to do. He runs to the gate and waits for his owner to take him home. Whether to fight or not is purely in the bull's domain, and such fights rarely result in serious injury.

When not in the ring the bulls lead pampered lives and the human owners devote most of their time to rearing and caring for them. The men even sleep alongside their prize fighters.

Similar contests are staged in Bolivia among the cattle of the Quechua Indians. Here the bulls are simply brought together on a dried-up river bed and allowed to fight as their nature takes them. In another part of southern Thailand, sheep are the focus of a similar gladiatorial skirmish.

The rams fight by lowering their heads and running towards each other. Although the resultant smack resounds around the arena the rams retreat to try again. Each head-thumping collision has an impact of around 10 miles an hour but the ram's skull, cushioned by air-filled cavities, is designed to

Overleaf: In Thailand bulls follow their natural urge to fight,
for the entertainment of human spectators.

*Although the bullfights can be violent, they rarely result in
serious injury and the bulls decide when the fight should end.*

absorb the shock. Even so, after five or more minutes of sparring, one of the
rams has usually had enough and rapidly retreats. The fight is then stopped.

Unlike the now extinct ancestors of cattle, wild sheep still survive and
each November, in the mountains of Corsica and Sardinia, mouflons spar
with each other on remote cliffs and crags. The outcome decides which ram
has control of the flock. Similarly, in captivity the most successful fighters
are also the ones most favoured for breeding.

Although in Thailand and Bolivia humans organise and control the
fighting of both sheep and cattle, the animals are simply doing what their
natural instincts compel them to. As they make the decision when the fight
should end, they suffer no more injuries than they would in the wild. Although
from a Western perspective such fights might seem cruel, from the viewpoint
of the animals involved, they have a more fulfilled life than that enjoyed by
the majority of domesticated animals. On farms, breeding males are now
often kept away from other animals and used simply as a source of semen for
artificial insemination.

Rams have air-filled cavities in their skulls to absorb the impact
of their head-banging tournaments.

SPURRING PARTNERS

IN BALI, THE VILLAGE bustle of people, dogs and careering mopeds has avian spectators. Through the lattice of wicker baskets, the descendants of Indian jungle fowl peer out on what to them is a familiar scene. Each day, these cock birds are placed alongside the road and, from this busy vantage point, they become accustomed to human activity. Frequently they are taken from the basket to be fed and caressed by their owners. Much of the spare time of Balinese men is given over to the breeding and rearing of these birds, which they use for fighting.

Contests between the cocks have religious significance and officially sanctioned fights take place in temple grounds. Once removed from their basket the cocks will not tolerate another male near them. Their only desire is to fight. Sharpened metal spurs are attached to the birds' natural spurs and the cocks are then made to face each other. Immediately, they puff up their neck feathers in an intimidating display. In the wild, this impressive

In Bali cock-fighting is highly ritualised. It invariably results
in death for the loser.

show may cause a smaller bird to run away, but the fighting cocks have been matched for size and so a skirmish is inevitable. As they leap in the air they twist their body to expose their lethal spurs. On their descent, the spurs slash at their opponents and often inflict lethal wounds.

The ritual, which is common throughout Indonesia, has developed in a culture in which plant life, particularly rice, plays a central role. Animals are generally held in low esteem. Significantly, the spilt blood is regarded as a sacrifice that will appease evil spirits and ensure a successful harvest. Inevitably, the fights also attract betting and are often held without religious sanction away from the temples.

In contrast, in Buddhist-influenced Thailand the cocks are not given artificial spurs and it is less common for the fights to end in death. The losing bird simply retreats. In Europe, cockfighting, using sharpened spurs, became common in the Middle Ages, when people were growing increasingly isolated from the natural world. It was at this time that other violent contests, such as pitting a dog against a bear or other wild animal, became common.

IT'S THE PITS

ACROSS EUROPE MASTIFFS WERE used to fight captured wild animals. But in England bulls were the preferred bait and they required a smaller, more nimble breed of dog to tackle them. The contest depended on the dog immobilising the bull by clinging persistently onto its snout. It had to avoid the bull's horns and withstand frequent tossing. The bulldog, developed by crossing the mastiff with other breeds, had the required characteristics of a tenacious nature coupled with agility. Pit bull terriers were created by subsequent selective breeding that further heightened their pugnacity. These were now most often pitted against each other.

In 1835 a law was passed in England that banned the use of fighting dogs but the pit bull terrier continued to fight in America, where an even more lethal strain was bred. Since the American pit bull terrier was recently introduced to Britain it has become the central player in a dog-fighting revival. Genetically transformed by human manipulation, these fighting dogs are usually loyal to their owners but they exhibit the lethal tendency to attack people or other dogs without warning.

These dogs bear little resemblance to any animal found in nature. The people who keep them for fighting, often from the most urbanised and socially depressed backgrounds, embody contemporary alienation from the natural world. It was this kind of separation that caused another contest involving bulls to flourish in Spain. Here, rather than facing dogs, the bull was pitted against a human adversary.

DEATH IN THE AFTERNOON

SPANISH FIGHTING BULLS ARE also specially bred for their pugnacity. They lead a contented and unfettered existence for most of their lives, roaming free on choice grazing lands. Only at the ritual surrounding his death does the bull come into contact with humans.

From the point of capture to the time he arrives in the bullring the bull is a frightened animal. With little previous contact with people his natural reaction is to regard all humans as dangerous. This is exactly what the ceremony requires and over the centuries the bull has been selectively bred to have a highly strung nature. In case there is any doubt, as soon as the animal is driven into the ring, a barbed and decorated dart is thrust into his neck. Enraged and confused, the bull then encounters the encircling crowd.

Like most herbivores, his eyesight is poor but it picks up the slightest movement. As the cheers of the crowd attract his attention he looks for any sign of motion that may signal a predator. The matador's assistants, the banderilleros, attempt to gain the bull's attention by waving their capes. With no retreat possible the bull turns to face the danger and may attempt to defend himself by charging the moving capes. The matador watches the bull's behaviour and after a few minutes takes over from the banderilleros.

The matador's performance is judged on how carefully he can choreograph the bull's charges and, by drifting the cape a few centimetres from the bull's horns, he confuses the bull into charging at the only visible source of danger – the red cape. The bull's vision is similar to that of a red-green colour-blind human, so the red hue has little significance to him – instead it is the movement that attracts his eye. These confusing and frightening encounters last only a few minutes before picadors riding on padded horses enter the ring.

The picador's role is to provoke the bull into charging his well-armoured horse and, at the last moment, to drive a long pike into the bull's neck muscles. After three such woundings, the injuries inflicted on his neck cause the bull to drop his head. Before the final encounter the banderilleros attempt to enliven and adorn the bull by driving wooden sticks, decorated with coloured paper, into his neck. It is now that the bull, weakened from the loss of blood, faces the matador again.

The matador now aims flamboyantly to show his skill at dominating the wounded creature. If the bull is sufficiently disorientated the matador will even turn his back on him and swagger away in a movement that emphasises this domination. The bull is finally killed as he desperately attempts to charge the matador and becomes impaled by a sword driven between his shoulderblades. If this fails to penetrate the vital organs, the

The Spanish bullfight has evolved into an intricate sequence of rituals which aim to glorify the domination of humans over wild animals.

sword is withdrawn and a second attempt made, or a short sword is brought out to perform the *coup de grâce*.

Bullfighting, which most people now recognise as cruel, was introduced into Spain in the eleventh century at a time when an increasing proportion of Spanish people were moving into towns. The ritual served to stress the separation of these people from the natural world they were trying to leave behind. It emphasised the domination of humanity over nature. Although the bull is a domesticated animal, the performance relies on the fact that he has been reared to have the nature of a wild beast. In this confrontation, the matador, in killing the bull, states his human superiority.

This spectacle signified a complete change of attitude both from that of Egyptian and earlier times when the bull was venerated as a god and that of the Minoan civilisation of Crete. Then, bulls were held in similar esteem and, pre-echoing the bull-leaping still practised in southern France, human gymnasts displayed their skills by leaping over the bull's horns.

The idea of dominating nature became more entrenched as increasing human populations were concentrated into villages and towns. With no contact at all with the animals and plants that sustained them, they were able to imagine that they had no connection with the natural world at all. The most drastic changes coincided with the Renaissance, when an even more human-centred world view emerged. The developing philosophies, including Descartes' assertion that animals were no more than machines, helped justify the cruelty that was frequently imposed on them.

Although many cruel sports are now banned by law, events that celebrate the domination of humans over animals still continue. In North America the rodeo fulfils this role.

BUCKING BRONCOS

THE RODEO HAD ITS origins in the Texas cattle-driving days when horses were broken for riding by bronco-busting. Rough riders overcame the horses' defensive bucking response by endurance. By staying on the animal, they aimed to conquer it both physically and spiritually. In the process they were able to impress on the horse the idea of human supremacy and once this was achieved the broken creature was ready to respond to the will of humans.

Rodeo arose as a celebration of this method of conquering a wild animal and has developed into a popular spectacle. In traditional riding, known as

In North America the rodeo first emerged as a celebration of the conquering of wild and untamed creatures. Today it is a big entertainment business.

saddle-bronc, the nervous and unbroken horse is dressed with a cut-down saddle and rope rein. As soon as it feels the unfamiliar presence of a man on its back it begins to buck. To ensure this reaction a leather strap is first tightened round the animal's flank to cause it pain. It jumps, and as soon as its feet touch the ground it feels further pain from the rider's spurs. The rider attempts to stay on the horse by maintaining a rhythm with the horse's bucking motion.

The popularity of these contests suggests that the desire to prove the superiority of humans over animals is still strong. The audience shows little sympathy for the animals involved and applauds their domination. These events have arisen in a culture which emphasises the distinction between people and other animals. It is an extension of the philosophy of conquering nature that motivated the pioneers of the American frontier. Such a view contrasts strongly with the beliefs of the cultures they replaced. The American Plains Indians, like other people living close to the natural world, had respect for the life around them and considered that they were part of it, rather than believing they were above it.

Even when hunting, they had respect for the animals they killed, thus contrasting sharply with the way that people in the cultures that have developed away from nature regard the animals that they hunt.

THE UNSPEAKABLE AND THE UNEATABLE

HUNTING HAS BEEN AN occupation of men since prehistoric times, but these early people had a practical reason to kill their food. The hunting tribes that still exist today are driven by the same needs. These people enjoy hunting, but they spare the lives of animals they have no reason to kill and they never hunt an animal simply for sport or because it could be considered dangerous to them. Even animals that are hunted for food are treated with respect and, after they have been killed, the hunters often enact rituals to help assuage the feelings of guilt. Part of this ceremony is to apologise to the animal concerned.

Hunting in industrialised societies is partly motivated by a desire to renew contact with the natural world but, removed from its original purpose and without the corresponding cultural reference, it often involves simply satisfying a desire to conquer it. Big-game hunting in Africa is motivated by this craving to pit humans against what are perceived as dangerously exciting wild animals.

In the United States, Australia and much of Europe, hunting is orientated towards free-living animals, and those considered dangerous are the ones preferred. But in the absence of larger prey, any type of animal may be considered fair game, and in Italy, France and Malta inoffensive migrating songbirds and hawks become targets. In Malta alone 50 000 birds of prey are shot each year.

In Britain and some other parts of Europe the main prey animals are specially bred for the purpose. This creates an interesting paradox, because many of the species concerned have profited from the relationship.

THE NUMBERS GAME

AS A COMMON PHEASANT forages for food in an English coppice it is behaving for all the world like a wild bird. It may have spent all its life in the wild or, alternatively, after passing the first few weeks of its life in a pen it was given its freedom. Although at liberty, regular supplies of grain mean that it rarely strays far from these human handouts.

The pheasant encounters few natural enemies, as most have been shot or trapped to protect it, but at some stage it will have to face a human predator. Its first confrontation is with the human's traditional canine hunting partner.

The dog tracks down the pheasant using scent and attacks by bursting through the undergrowth. The bird's short wings whirr it into the air. It escapes, but as it soars over the trees it catches sight of the familiar shapes of humans below. If unlucky, this view is the last it sees, for a shotgun blast will take it out of the sky. But many escape and over the shooting season only one in three of released pheasant are brought down by shotgun fire. The escaping birds and the continual restocking from reared stocks means that the pheasant is a common bird across Europe and a large part of North America. Its natural habitat is restricted to parts of Asia, from the Black Sea to southern China, and so, ironically, the species has profited from becoming a modern game animal.

Red grouse have similarly gained from the protection given by sportsmen and in the Scottish Highlands red deer are maintained at unnaturally high population levels because they provide quarry for hunters. From the viewpoint of the animals that are hunted it makes little difference if their lives are ended by humans or by other predators. What is significant for the species is the amount of protection they are given while they are alive and the population levels that they are able to maintain.

Often the artificially high populations encouraged by hunting cause other animals to suffer. Not only are competing predators trapped or shot but the animals themselves may affect the local environment. In the Scottish Highlands, due to the grazing of red deer protected for hunting, the natural regeneration of Scot's pine has effectively ceased.

The imbalances caused by game animals are most apparent when they have been transported to different lands. Nearly a quarter of all extinctions of mammals and a fifth of those of birds have been caused by alien animals introduced by humans. Although some of these introductions were for aesthetic reasons the majority were for sport. Once the game animals found themselves away from their natural competitors their populations often multiplied to spectacular proportions. Some of the most disastrous results were seen in Australia.

AUSTRALIAN IMMIGRANTS

FOXES WERE AMONG THE animals introduced into countries like Australia to make up for imagined deficiencies in the local fauna. They flourished at the expense of the indigenous marsupial population: animals such as possums and kangaroos were no match for such an aggressive alien predator. Introduced deer showed a similar disastrous increase. But the most spectacular and catastrophic sporting introduction involved rabbits.

In 1859 in a country estate near Geelong, Victoria, 24 rabbits were released to provide game for shooting parties. They rapidly reproduced and soon moved into New South Wales, where by 1890 the population had reached such a level that 10 million were destroyed in a single year. This hardly dented their numbers and, as they spread across Australia, they began turning grassland into desert. Nothing stopped their advance until, in 1950, myxomatosis, introduced by humans and carried by the rabbit flea, caused the population to be almost wiped out. The few that remained had an immunity to the virus and slowly their numbers rose again. Today, helped by three successive years of high rainfall and lush pasture, the rabbits in New South Wales are back in plague proportions.

For the rabbits the outcome, as the dry season begins, is bleak. Life for these animals becomes a continuous quest for something to eat. Literally millions are involved in the same frantic searching and any green foliage vanishes into a multitude of ravenous mouths. The bark of any tree in reach of their outstretched bodies is stripped away and soon, over thousands of square kilometres, every edible fragment has been consumed.

The rabbits' desperate hunger is combined with an insatiable thirst. The plague peaks at the end of the rainy season and swarms of desperate rabbits encircle the disappearing water holes. Water, evaporating under the ferocious heat, vanishes even faster down the rabbits' thirsty throats. Once the water and the vegetation have been swallowed up, the starving rabbits begin to die. Soon the arid landscape is littered with millions of their emaciated bodies, a grisly testament to the long-term consequences of an

*Recent rabbit plagues in Australia are the result of 24
animals being released about 130 years ago, to improve
shooting prospects.*

apparently innocent attempt to improve hunting prospects.

The ecological devastation wrought by the rabbits' infestation is compounded by other introduced animals that reach similar plague levels. These are encouraged and watered by humans so their population never suffers the same spectacular failure as that of the rabbit. They cause even greater environmental damage. These invasive and consuming animals are sheep and cattle.

PLAGUE LIVESTOCK

IN AUSTRALIA, A HALF of all existing arid areas have been severely damaged by the overgrazing of livestock. An incredible 2 million square kilometres have suffered from their depredations and a further 750 000 square kilometres of semi-arid land have been similarly impoverished.

The impact of domesticated animals on the world's landscape began as soon as the relationship with these creatures developed around 9000 years ago. As numbers increased they began to affect the local vegetation: either it was cleared to make way for the expanding herds or it was literally consumed by their voracious mouths.

In the early days, goats were the most destructive of these domesticated animals because they could graze from shrubs inaccessible to other livestock. What they could not reach from the ground, they climbed up to consume. Often they were grazed on land that already suffered from the effects of low rainfall and, as the vegetation disappeared, they transformed this parched land to desert. Much of the desertification of Africa has been caused by the overgrazing of these and other domesticated animals.

Today, a seventh of the weight of all existing land mammals is accounted for by those we have domesticated, four times the weight of all humanity. These three billion organisms have prospered at the expense of other animals and have become a ravenous and all-consuming machine. This is exactly how many creatures are treated – as mechanical sources of protein.

ASSAULT AND BATTERY

SOME OF THE ANIMALS to suffer most have been the descendants of the red jungle fowl that was attracted to villages in North India about 4000 years ago. They eventually spread across the world, usually living free and unfettered lives as scavengers around hamlets and farms. But in the industrialised world they have not fared as well: they are now regarded as just another component in the food-producing machinery.

The process starts as soon as they leave the egg, at the time they would naturally imprint on their parent. Instead they are removed from the incubator and immediately placed on a conveyor belt. Their journey is soon interrupted by human sorters and, depending on their sex, they are either thrown back onto the conveyor belt or into a basket. From the chicks' viewpoint it is difficult to know which are the lucky ones. Those in the basket are males and, if they have not suffocated through the weight of others on top of them, they will be gassed when the basket is full. The females on the conveyor belt have a much longer life ahead of them, but in the role of battery chickens.

Today, the huge populations of livestock that sustain us are causing environmental change. In Australia, sheep have created vast deserts.

Chickens, modern-day descendants of the Indian jungle fowl,
lead a mechanised existence that prevents them from enjoying
any elements of a natural life.

Crammed into cages that are too small to permit them to turn, and at densities so high that they have no alternative but to attack their neighbours, they spend their whole lives standing on a wire grid. They are kept in perpetual artificial light but never see daylight. Their meals arrive on a conveyor belt, so the opportunities for normal foraging behaviour are non-existent and, each time they lay an egg, it rolls to the back of the cage where another conveyor takes it away. They are no longer treated as animals with even the minimum rights to an expression of a natural life. They have become deliberately mechanised even though their natural behaviour has shown no corresponding change.

Of the seven billion chickens in the world most are now kept under these intensive conditions. In Britain and America there is one battery chicken for every living person.

The rest of the domesticated animals have varying degrees of freedom ranging from the battery-like conditions of factory pigs to the ranch-style rearing of beef cattle. Although the free-ranging animals have a better life, their numerical success has been at the expense of other organisms. Together with the plants grown as crops they have caused drastic change.

REAP THE WHIRLWIND

AS EXISTING VEGETATION WAS cleared for agriculture, the trans-formations of the landscape produced problems of their own. The soil of most agricultural land erodes five times faster than that of uncultivated land. The dustbowls created in the American Middle West in the 1930s were graphic illustrations of what could happen if cereal crops were simply planted in place of existing well-adapted vegetation.

But many of the changes that have taken place are too complex for a neat understanding of cause and effect. The destruction of rainforests, often to provide land to grow unsuitable crops or graze cattle, can affect global rainfall patterns.

Even the crops can influence the balance of the gasses of the atmosphere. Rice, a grass with a 6000-year-old history of cultivation, is now so widespread that the marsh gas, known as methane, discharged from bacteria in paddy fields has an appreciable effect on global warming. Termites that have multiplied spectacularly as consumers of agricultural plants also release significant quantities of this greenhouse gas. Even the digestive processes of the billion or so cows in the world belch out damaging amounts of methane.

Although much of agriculture is used to maintain human populations, a surprising quantity is used to sustain the swelling multitude of domesticated animals. A staggering 86 per cent of North American grain is fed to them.

The human population is now supported by a handful of plants and animals domesticated less than 10 000 years ago. These animal partners have allowed people to live apparently distanced from other organisms, but they affect the world in ways few of us can envisage. The people they support are now isolated from the ecological consequences of their way of living.

KAYAPO ECOLOGY

IN BRAZIL A MACAW FLIES over the smouldering remnants of what was once prime rainforest. The holocaust is the result of a drive to intensify beef

Overleaf: As the Amazon is irretrievably destroyed to provide short-term pasture for cattle, the human and animal inhabitants, who once lived in perfect harmony with their environment, are rapidly disappearing.

A Kayapo woman prepares Açaí.

production to supply the world's meat markets. The smoky remains will soon be replaced by quick-growing clump grass to provide short-term pasture for cattle. After a succession of burning, reseeding and grazing of the land over a few years, the productivity will be exhausted and the soil will be devastated.

For the thousands of species that have made the rainforest their home, this destruction is an irreversible catastrophe. The macaw, at least, can retreat from the advancing apocalypse. It flies into the forest that still remains. The jungle canopy, verdant and festooned with lianas, spreads out like a mossy awning beneath it. As the bird flies, it sees few tears or slashes in its green surface – only the occasional emergent tree breaks through. But suddenly an opening appears. Beneath, arranged in a circle, is a variety of structures made from leaves and branches. These are the dwellings of the Kayapo Indians.

Unlike the cultures that are steadily encroaching on them, the Kayapo's lives are still entwined with the life that sustains them. Their understanding of this life is truly remarkable. They are not only aware of which plants can be used for nourishment, which are poisonous and which are medicines, but they have an almost encyclopaedic knowledge of the animals that supply them with food. Of these, the most important are social insects, particularly bees.

A TASTE OF HONEY

BEES GIVE THE KAYAPO many provisions. Honey, pollen and larvae are eaten. Wax and resin are used in handicrafts. Pupae and parts of bees, such as stings and mandibles, are used for medicine. The Kayapo appreciate the remarkable complexity of the bees' lives, recognising that in organisation and demarcation of labour these insect societies resemble those of humans. But rather than regarding it as an inferior version, the Kayapo believe that the bees' way of living is something to aspire to. They actually model their own lives on those of the bees. Such knowledge was thought to have been acquired by an ancient shaman who taught their ancestors how to live after studying the bees' behaviour.

Today, the Kayapo still believe that their traditional circular village is arranged like the cross-section of a conical bees' nest. They recognise that the way human labour is shared in the village has its counterpart in the different castes of the beehive. Warrior bees defend the nest, just as male warriors defend the village. Worker bees collect pollen and nectar, just as the women go out to gather the fruits of the forest. Like human scouts, some bees specialise in searching for food and looking for new nest locations.

The Kayapo also recognise a bee chief at the centre of the nest, who coordinates and orders the activity of the colony. This bee is known scientifically as the queen and she indeed has this function, using scent to communicate messages to the rest of the hive. The Kayapo believe the bee chief has wives who are in charge of egg-laying and the care of children. These are what entomologists would call nurse bees.

The Kayapo understand that the bees have insect companions. They are regarded as the bees' equivalent to the village dogs and are believed to carry out the same scavenging function. They are actually a type of mite and they may well have this beneficial role.

Kayapo shamans can recognise 56 varieties of stingless bees and can even identify species that have no practical importance. Nine of the species are kept in a semidomesticated state around the village. Kayapo find new hives by listening for the calls of bee-eating birds, or by hours spent observing the flight patterns of the insects as they visit flowers for nectar or river beds for water. They are also remarkably attuned to the smell of the bees. They can follow the invisible odour trails left by swarms and foraging scout bees as though they were the spoor of a game animal.

Once a new hive has been located, the Kayapo may wait as long as ten years before they open the hive to take the honey. This understanding of the need to conserve typifies the Kayapo's appreciation of the forest ecology. Flowers favoured by the bees are left to grow and may even be planted in gardens or along forest trails. Once established, some beehives are harvested year after year. The Kayapo remove only a portion of the contents and, to ensure that the hive survives, brood combs, honey and pollen are returned to the nests.

To reach nests on trees too tall to climb, they may chop down the tree to retrieve the nest. Rather than being wasteful, and in contrast to the clear-felling devastating other parts of the rainforest, this cutting of single trees opens up small clearings that allow the sun to penetrate. Soon new plants grow up in their place and this helps increase the natural forest diversity. The Kayapo also cultivate food or medicinal plants in the clearings and birds and game animals are attracted there too.

The Kayapo are so tuned to the life of the forest that they hold it in deep respect, but their attitude is also practical and unsentimental. They hunt animals for food but they treat these animals with reverence, realising that their own survival depends on the species' continued well-being. Young creatures that have been orphaned by hunting are taken back to the village and reared as pets. Parrots are particularly popular companions and their most colourful feathers, often removed without harming the bird, are used to decorate the Kayapo's spectacular head-dresses.

TROUBLE IN PARADISE

FOR THOUSANDS OF YEARS the Kayapo have lived in harmony with the forest. Out of all the forest animals, bees excited the greatest admiration, for they appeared to lead the most exemplary lives. Then, in 1966, at the time of a full moon, a new variety of bee arrived that had less admirable qualities. These bees were more aggressive than the existing residents and they attacked and pillaged other hives. They were also dangerous. If a person approached the hive and was stung, a chemical signal was sent to the other bees which caused them to attack en masse with ferocious stings.

The Kayapo believe that their society mimics that of stingless bees.

Significantly, these deadly bees were not native to the forest but came from the world outside. They had been created by crossing the aggressive but mildly stinging African honey bee – the same species that the Boran honey-gatherers and the honey-guide depend on – with the benign but powerfully armed domestic bee. This experiment in crossbreeding a vigorous new form of bee went badly awry.

The new genetic strains retained the aggressive nature of the African bee but coupled it with an even deadlier sting. After being introduced into South America, these killer bees spread northwards until eventually they entered the life of the Kayapo. Like an omen, they provided a foretaste of many of the dangers to come. The killer bees were followed by alien diseases to which the Kayapo had no natural immunity. Colds, 'flu and measles were all potentially lethal to them.

Today the rainforest that shelters the Kayapo is attacked by other deadly forces brought in from the external world. The way of life of the Kayapo is under threat from deforestation and pressures from the encroaching human culture outside.

GLOBAL WARNING

THE HUMAN POPULATIONS that now unwittingly threaten the Kayapo believe that they can exist with no reference to the natural world. But the consequences of their daily lives penetrate as far as the Brazilian rainforest. The contrast between the Kayapo and the inhabitants of the urban jungle could not be greater. The people of the city have now totally lost touch with other life.

The process began when humanity became caught up in the relationships with plants that gave rise to agriculture. It continued as these people settled and developed similar relationships with animals. Initially, the partnership between these domesticated species and people was close, even reverential, but as these plants and animals supplied the food that enabled human numbers to increase, the majority of people began to live physically isolated from them.

The respect for other creatures started to disappear. This changing attitude to animals was reflected in developing religious belief, with only Eastern religions retaining links with the animal world.

As towns and cities grew, an increasing percentage of people were removed from direct contact with animals. Their only visible nonhuman companions were their pets which, significantly, continued to be treated with indulgence. This apparent physical isolation fostered a belief that humans were in some way separate from the natural world. But we need look no further than the ecology of our own bodies to discover that we are not alone.

Even the most hygienically scrubbed and disinfected body entertains millions of organisms that are so perfectly adapted to their host that they cause no discomfort. The bacteria that live on the skin, the mites that inhabit the hair follicles and the single-celled organisms that live inside the intestines all make their homes on people without causing any harm. Some of them are vital to their host's survival. Sometimes the human body is invaded by organisms with which we have yet to reach such harmonious agreement, and these cause symptoms of disease or even kill.

The earth can similarly be regarded as a living organism. Humans are but one of literally millions of species that make up its vital body. Together this life creates an infinitely complex web of interacting components that work together to keep the earth healthy. Humans are but one element in this super-organism. At one time they were as benign as the bacteria or the follicle mites that inhabit the human skin, but through the relationships they have developed with a handful of other organisms, their numbers and those of their domesticated partners have expanded to perilous proportions.

Unlike the Kayapo Indians, people in the developed world, and the life they have promoted, no longer live in a harmonious balance with the earth. They resemble a parasite out of sympathy with its host. We can never return to the hunting and gathering existence exemplified by the Kayapo, Hagerhai, Bushmen, or any other group that still continues the ancestral way of life. But we can learn from them the need to live in balance with the other plants and animals of the planet. Unless we succeed in this we will end up destroying the world that sustains us. And, unlike the organisms that invade our bodies, if we kill this host there is nowhere else for us to go.

A Kayapo Indian making a ceremonial head-dress with parrot feathers.

INDEX

Page numbers in *italic* refer to the illustrations